Wild flowers

THEIR HABITATS IN
BRITAIN AND NORTHERN EUROPE

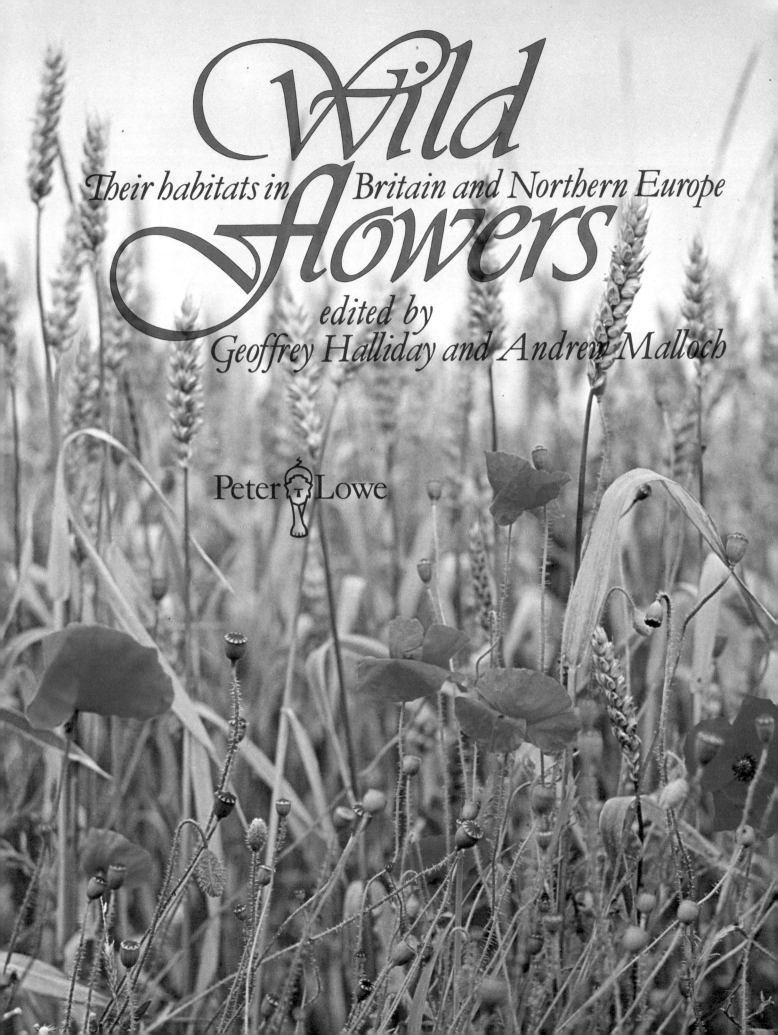

Wild flowers

Their habitats in Britain and Northern Europe

edited by
Geoffrey Halliday and Andrew Malloch

Peter Lowe

Title page: Common poppies (*Papaver rhoeas*) in a field of wheat.
Page 10: The tall purple flowers of the foxglove *(Digitalis purpurea)* which typically grows in hedgerows, on roadsides and at the edges of woodlands in the western parts of the region.

British Library Cataloguing in Publication Data
Halliday, G.
  Wild Flowers.
  1. Wild Flowers – Europe
  I. Title   II. Malloch, A.
  582′.13′094   QK281

Printed and bound in Great Britain by
©ollins, Glasgow

ISBN 0 85654 618 6

Contents

Foreword

The past ten years have seen a plethora of books concerning the flowers of Europe and Scandinavia come not only into our bookshops but even into the ranks of best-sellers. Many of these are no more than descriptions of the plants both in words and pictures, with notes about their geographical distribution, habitats and, in rare cases, the vegetation of which they form a part.

During this time no books have appeared at a popular level concerning the vegetation itself. There are a number of books and even series of books which do deal with certain major habitats and their ecosystems, including descriptions of the plants and animals which typify them. There are also great tomes on the vegetation itself which, with all respect, only make light reading for the dedicated expert. This is to my knowledge the only book which provides an adequate yet readable description of the vegetation of this important and diverse part of the world.

The team of writers is as impressive as the work they have produced. Professor Hugo Sjörs is one of the great exponents of the Scandinavian School of Phytosociology (the subject which deals with the description and classification of vegetation). He, above all others, has inspired his many followers to use that discipline as a basis for understanding the ecology of the vegetation. Professor Donald Pigott has upheld the traditions of the British School of Ecology founded by Sir Arthur Tansley which from the outset attempted to understand vegetation through the study of its component plants.

The other authors are equally distinguished in their specialities, which cover all the principal habitats of the region, forests, heaths, grassland, mountains, mires, salt marshes, sand-dunes and shingle beaches, sea cliffs and man-made wasteland. This is not, however, just a series of isolated chapters, objects and opinions. Like the vegetation it describes, it is a working whole, much more than the sum of its component parts.

The vegetation of Europe is part of a chain of life which spans the environments of the world, using the sun's energy to increase organic production and providing habitats for the world's wildlife. As such it must form the basis of all conservation measures and set a pattern for the future wise use of the resources of this planet.

This book can only help further the layman's understanding of these matters and hence aid the cause of conservation. It is also a welcome addition to the libraries of all those institutes of learning which teach geography, biology and environmental science.

It is with great pleasure that I write this Foreword and note that the list of authors includes my teachers, colleagues and students.

David Bellamy
Department of Botany
Durham University

I
Introduction to the region

North-west Europe is notable for its varied range of natural and semi-natural habitats. These include deciduous and coniferous forests, mountains, moorlands and grasslands, lakes, rivers and mires, sand-dunes and coasts. The different habitats support a wide variety of plants and animal communities of varying degrees of individuality and exclusiveness. This book is concerned with the plant communities, their characteristic features and their more interesting species. These communities are not simply academic concepts but are the very basis of our countryside and as such are widely enjoyed by naturalists and the general public.

North-west Europe is not a well-defined geographical region since it lacks natural boundaries to the south and east. It has therefore been necessary to adopt certain rather arbitrary limits separating it from the Mediterranean area, the Alps and eastern Europe, with their very distinctive floras. These limits extend from the estuary of the Gironde on the French Atlantic coast, north-eastwards across France to the Rhine, to include the Vosges but not the Black Forest with its similarity to the Alps, and then across central Germany to the Oder, which forms the eastern boundary. Poland and the Baltic states are excluded but Scandinavia and Finland are within the limits.

In many areas the distribution of present-day habitats is largely the result of the interaction of topography, climate and vegetational history, often subsequently profoundly modified by man's activities. Before considering the habitats individually, it is therefore necessary to describe briefly the variation and effects of these three primary factors in north-west Europe.

Wood anemones *(Anemone nemorosa)* can form a superb white carpet on the floor of woodlands growing on rich, brown forest soils. Flowering period: March-May.

The Vosges are amongst the highest mountains in the mainland part of the region but are sufficiently far south for trees to cover the rounded slopes and hill tops, although some of the flat summits have pasture and mires. Most of the agriculture is confined to the flat valley floors or lower hill slopes.

Topography and geology

A broad lowland belt runs from south-west to north-east across the region and through it meander the major rivers of north-west Europe: the Loire, Seine, Thames, Rhine and Elbe. The rocks here are mostly of Mesozoic age (64 to 225 million years old). Predominantly soft and often rich in lime, they have weathered to produce the characteristic gently rolling landscape that is to be found in southern England and much of northern France.

At the western end of the English Channel, both to the north and south, there are older, Palaeozoic, uplands formed by the violent Hercynian earth-movements which occurred around 280 million years ago, at the end of the Carboniferous period. In Brittany and south-west England these uplands are formed mainly of hard granitic rocks but the spectacular coastal mountains of south-west Ireland are largely composed of Devonian sedimentary rocks (345 to 410 million years old). To the east the Mesozoic rocks tend to disappear beneath a blanket of glacial and glacial-outwash deposits, mainly sands and gravels, and also wind-blown loess. These deposits produce the flat, featureless scenery characteristic of the north German plain and Jutland.

To the south of these lowlands, the land gradually rises and there are several small mountain areas, varying in height from 700–1200m, such as the Ardenne, Eifel, Thüringer Wald, Harz and Vosges. The Vosges are the highest, dominating the western side of the upper part of the Rhine rift valley as the Black Forest does the eastern. All these mountains are rounded and mostly wooded, but there are extensive areas of grassland and mire on the more poorly drained plateaux. Like the hills of Brittany, they are formed of Palaeozoic rocks which were affected by the Hercynian earth movements, but were then extensively eroded, overlain by later sedimentary rocks and finally raised by the great Alpine earth movements during the mid-Tertiary period (c.30 million years ago). The Eifel is remarkable for its volcanic features, eruptions having continued there from the Tertiary into the Stone Age, only about 12,000 years ago.

Left: Soft rocks give the rolling landscape of southern England and northern France. Here the once sheep-grazed grasslands of the chalk are bounded by improved agricultural grassland and are being colonized by trees and shrubs including hawthorn (*Crataegus monogyna*), field maple (*Acer campestre*), whitebeam (*Sorbus aria*), privet (*Ligustrum vulgare*), ash (*Fraxinus excelsior*) and the dog rose (*Rosa canina*).

The very old rocks of much of Finland and eastern Sweden have been worn down to a gently sloping plain, now covered by many lakes. Here the lakes are separated from one another by sinuous mounds of peat on which grow scots pines (*Pinus sylvestris*) and shrubby heaths.

In the north-east of the area, occupying most of Finland and Sweden, is the Baltic Shield. This is a vast area of ancient Precambrian gneissic and granitic rocks, dating from over 570 million years ago. Over hundreds of millions of years the rocks have been worn down to a gently inclined plain, covered with a myriad lakes and finally vanishing below the waters of the Baltic Sea. The Shield, particularly in the south-east, is covered with extensive glacial deposits, notably prominent moraines and sinuous eskers, the latter formed by subglacial rivers. Most of the land to the west of the Baltic Shield was profoundly affected by the Caledonian earth movements which occurred at the end of the Silurian period (about 410 million years ago). The rocks here are mainly Precambrian or Lower Palaeozoic and, like those of the Shield, are extremely hard. Folding and uplifting of these rocks produced the backbone of the Scandinavian mountains and those of the northern part of the British Isles from north-east Scotland south-westwards to Connemara in western Ireland. In the British Isles the highest summits lie within the range 1000–1300m but in Scandinavia there are several mountains, both in the north and south, which exceed 2000m. The scenery here is on a truly alpine scale with numerous valley glaciers and plateau ice-caps.

In western Scotland and northern Ireland there are extensive areas of more recent basaltic and volcanic rocks dating from the early Tertiary period (55–60 million years ago). The whole of the Faeroes consists of such rocks, as does much of western and eastern Iceland. Similar rocks in central Iceland are even younger, having been formed within the last million years, and volcanic eruptions still occur. The scenery of Iceland, although very dramatic, is less spectacular and alpine than that of Scandinavia. Iceland does, however, boast Europe's most impressive ice-caps, the largest, Vatnajökull, being 150km long.

The chemical nature of the rocks and of the soils derived from them is an important factor affecting the distribution of very many plants. The most important single factor is calcium. Limestone soils naturally have a very high calcium content but they are very low in almost every other essential nutrient, particularly in phosphorus, nitrogen and potassium. Other rocks, such as basalt, produce soils that are not only rich in calcium but also in potassium, sodium and magnesium, although they, too, may contain little phosphorus and nitrogen. Rocks and soils which are rich in the four elements, sodium, potassium, magnesium and calcium, but particularly the last, are usually described by ecologists as being base-rich. (This is really a mis-use of the chemical term base: these elements can form bases, but are not themselves bases.) Base-rich rocks may be quite widespread, as are the Icelandic basalts, but as a rule they occur locally in areas of otherwise base-poor rocks. Even if not actually exposed, calcareous or base-rich rocks may influence the vegetation if they are affected by percolating water. Where nutrient-enriched water reaches the surface it produces a calcareous or base-rich flush, supporting a characteristic vegetation.

Plants growing in base-rich soils are usually referred to as calcicole species, and in north-west Europe they greatly outnumber the so-called calcifuge species, which are associated with base-poor soils. Species are not necessarily restricted to calcareous or base-rich soils because of the plant nutrients themselves or because of the neutral or somewhat alkaline nature of the soils. Many southern European species, for example, are restricted to the chalk in northern France and southern England not because it is calcareous but because its soft, very permeable nature provides a relatively dry habitat for southern plants in a wet, northern climate.

The climate of north-west Europe

The climate of north-west Europe varies surprisingly little from season to season. This is due to its position in the path of the rain-laden westerly and south-westerly winds which move across the Atlantic to the south of the Icelandic low-pressure area. Since the sea temperature does not alter much from winter to summer, these maritime winds tend to warm the land in winter and cool it in summer. The winter warming is more pronounced than might be expected at this latitude because of the weak but nonetheless beneficial influence of the Gulf Stream. So whereas south-west Ireland, for example, has a mean January temperature of 7°C, that of the north coast of Newfoundland, lying at the same latitude, is only −12°C. Not surprisingly, the northern coast of Newfoundland has a subarctic vegetation while in south-west Ireland frost-sensitive plants such as the strawberry-tree (*Arbutus unedo*) and the naturalized fuchsia (*Fuchsia magellanica*) are able to flourish.

The mild, wet climate of the western coasts changes gradually towards the east. Whereas Brest, on the coast of Brittany, has a difference of only 10°C between its July and

North-west Europe can be divided into two climatic zones: the oceanic zone of high rainfall and small temperature range (1) and the continental zone of low rainfall and large temperature range (2). The distributions of bog asphodel (*Narthecium ossifragum*) and the small, gorse-like *Genista germanica* are strongly correlated with these climatic zones. Europe's third main climatic zone, the Mediterranean (3) lies outside our region and has its own distinctive range of plants.

Left: The mountains of Norway and Sweden, formed of old, resistant rocks, have been heavily glaciated in the past, and show evidence of this in the broad, steep sided, flat-bottomed valleys through which streams meander in ever changing channels.

Calcifuges are plants that avoid soils rich in calcium, being commonest on acid, nutrient-poor soils. Heather (*Calluna vulgaris*) is probably the best known example. Flowering period: July-September.

Left: Calcicoles are plants that are characteristically found on soils rich in calcium. Here, growing in grassland over chalk, is the common spotted orchid (*Dactylorhiza fuchsii*). The different plants show how much flower colour varies in this species. Flowering period : June to August.

January mean temperatures and a rainfall of 810 mm, Frankfurt an der Oder, on the German-Polish border, has comparable figures of 19°C and 520 mm, and this trend continues eastwards into Poland and Russia. These two contrasting climates—one wet, with a small annual temperature range, the other dry, with a large range—are termed respectively, oceanic and continental. None of the areas included in our region has a truly continental climate. Even in eastern Germany, the climate is more accurately described as subcontinental. Areas with a strongly marked oceanic climate receive most of their rain during the winter and the distribution of these areas in north-west Europe is shown on the map on page 16. The map also shows the effect of climate on the distribution of two plants: the bog asphodel (*Narthecium ossifragum*), an oceanic plant, has a western distribution which is largely complemented farther east by that of the subcontinental gorse-like plant *Genista germanica*. Very many plants of north-west Europe have distributions which reflect varying degrees of oceanicity or, less commonly, continentality. Not only does the flora change from west to east, but so also do the habitats. This is well illustrated by the different kinds of mire described in chapter 8.

It is not always obvious what particular climatic factor limits a plant's distribution. The eastern limit of the oceanic holly (*Ilex aquifolium*), for example, appears to be determined by the winter temperature, because it closely follows the January mean isotherm of 0°C. The winter isotherms are aligned north-south, due to the maritime influence of the violent Atlantic winter gales which penetrate far inland. By contrast, the July isotherms are aligned more or less from east to west, dipping slightly towards the Atlantic. The northern limit of the pedunculate oak (*Quercus robur*) in north-west Europe follows these east-west isotherms, indicating that the tree is sensitive to summer cold, whereas holly is limited by winter cold. The maritime influence shown by the north-south winter isotherms means that the Faeroes, for example, have a January mean of 4°C which is slightly higher than that of Venice, 2000 km to the south; but whereas Venice basks in a July mean temperature of 25°C, the comparable figure for the Faeroes is a mere 11°C.

The most extreme oceanic climates occur on the seaward side of the high mountains of Iceland, the British Isles and Scandinavia. Here are extensive areas with a precipitation of more than 1800 mm and locally over 3000 mm, with rain on two days out of three. Yet immediately behind these mountains as, for example, in north-east Iceland, north-east Scotland, and along the entire eastern side of the Scandinavian mountains, there are strongly contrasted drier, rain-shadow areas. It is a remarkable experience to travel along the Sognefjord, the largest fjord system in western Norway, and then to cross a mere 60 km over the mountains to the inland valleys, where the low rainfall of 270 mm has to be supplemented by irrigation. Yet not all areas of low precipitation are obvious rain-shadow or continental areas. One botanically important area is the Seine basin, where low rainfall and warm summers allow Mediterranean species such as the oak *Quercus pubescens* to reach their northernmost limits.

Over most of north-west Europe winters are relatively mild, and prolonged periods of frost and snow are rare. The result is an exceptionally long growing season for plants. Naturally, winters do become progressively more severe, more continental, from west to east, and spring and autumn become shorter. Brest has less than 40 days a year with frost, whereas Frankfurt an der Oder averages 190 days; the Rhine at Cologne is frozen for 13 days a year, the Oder for 43 days. In most years ice forms in the Kattegat, between Denmark and Sweden, and in the Baltic Sea, while the northern half of the Gulf of Bothnia freezes for nearly six months every year. Farther north, winters are longer and colder. The lowest winter temperatures occur in the subcontinental eastern valleys of the Scandinavian mountains and in the uplands around the Swedish-Finnish border: Karesuando, for example, has a mean January temperature of −15°C.

The penalty for a mild winter is a cool, cloudy and humid summer, in marked contrast to the clear skies, summer heat and drought of the Mediterranean area to the south or the plains of Poland and Russia to the east.

The natural vegetation over most of north-west Europe is forest—deciduous and broad-leaved to the south, coniferous to the north. Most broad-leaved trees, with the important exception of birch (*Betula* species), need warmer summers than conifers, and the boundary between the two types of forest is the northern limit of deciduous tree growth rather than the southern limit for conifers. This does not coincide closely with any particular climatic factor, but, in general, the colder the winter the warmer the summer must be for deciduous trees to grow; in other words, the shorter the growing season, the warmer it has to be. These natural forest zones are, of course, not confined to Europe, but occur over much of the temperate and boreal parts of the northern hemisphere.

Climate changes imperceptibly but inevitably with time. Throughout the Quaternary period or Ice Age (roughly the last two million years), Europe has been subjected to several major phases of glaciation. These were interrupted by warmer periods, interglacials, lasting from 10,000 to 50,000 years, during which climates were sometimes appreciably warmer than they are at the present time. During the

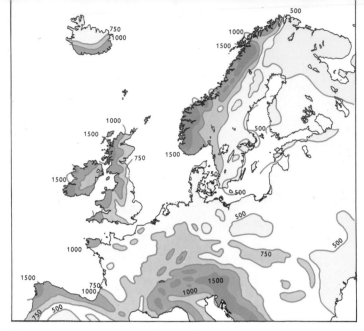

North-west Europe: Annual rainfall.

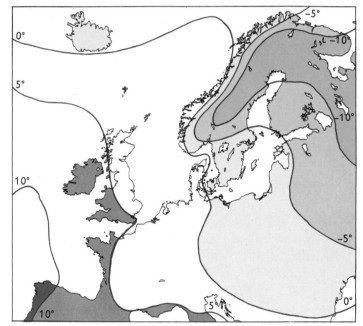

Mean temperatures for January (above) and July (below).

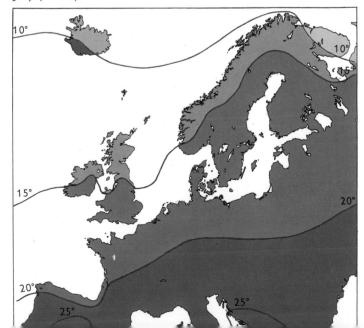

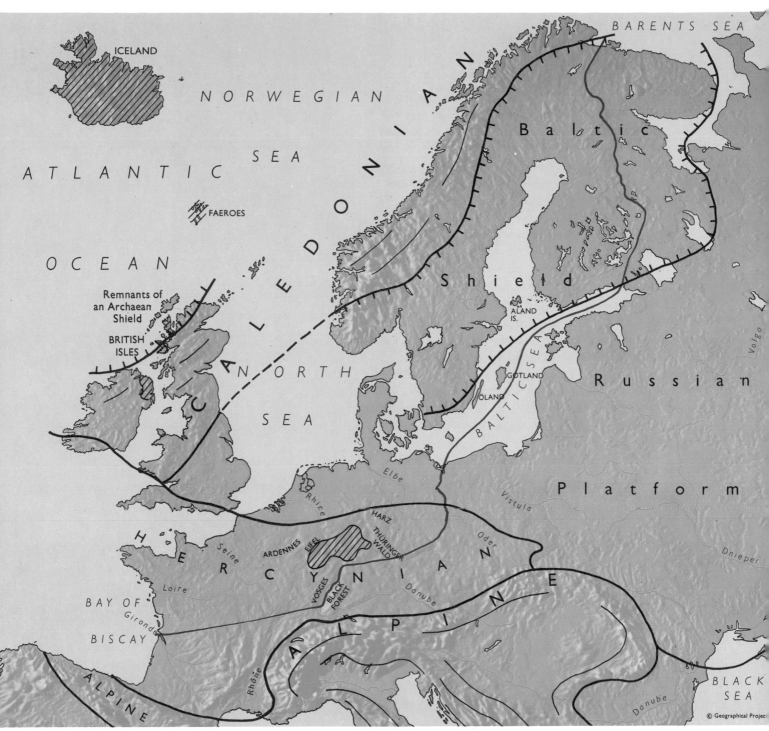

The map shows labels including: BARENTS SEA, ICELAND, NORWEGIAN SEA, ATLANTIC OCEAN, FAEROES, Baltic, Shield, Remnants of an Archaean Shield, BRITISH ISLES, NORTH SEA, ALAND IS., GOTLAND, OLAND, BALTIC SEA, Russian, Platform, Volga, Dnieper, CALEDONIAN, HERCYNIAN, ALPINE, Seine, Loire, Rhine, Elbe, Vistula, Oder, ARDENNES, EIFEL, HARZ, THÜRINGER WALD, VOSGES, BLACK FOREST, Danube, Gironde, BAY OF BISCAY, Rhône, Danube, BLACK SEA, © Geographical Project

North-west Europe, showing the relief of the region and the main areas of mountain building. Rocks vary in age from those of the ancient Archaean and Baltic Shields to those of volcanic areas (shown shaded): in Iceland eruptions still occur. The red line indicates the boundary of the region covered in the book.

Top left: In north-west Europe annual rainfall is highest on the west-facing coasts and lessens eastwards. Mountainous areas receive more than the plains that lie beside them.

Left centre and below: Over much of the region the isotherms tend to run north-south in January and east-west in July and the annual temperature range is larger in the east than in the west.

glaciations, the ice-fronts, whether generally advancing or retreating, were continually subjected to minor fluctuations. For this reason it is not possible to say definitely whether the relatively short period of time since the maximum extent of the last glaciation, about 18,000 years ago, represents the beginning of an interglacial or is merely an interlude in a continuing process of glaciation.

The history of the vegetation

Because of the vast extent of the last major glaciation, the flora of almost all the habitats in north-west Europe have developed only during the past 18,000 years. Fossil evidence shows that before the start of the Ice Age there was a greater variety of species in most north European habitats than exists there today. With every successive glaciation, warmth-demanding species were forced to migrate southwards. Some managed to escape to the warmer climates of the Mediterranean or south-east Europe. Others were caught between the advancing ice-sheet in the north and the mountains and smaller glaciers of central Europe and the Pyrenees.

The plants that remained in north-west Europe were predominantly hardy species of the open treeless tundra. When the climate eventually improved, these species returned northwards, and in their wake came those that were able to reinvade from the south and south-east. With each successive cycle of glaciation and interglacial the numbers of reinvading species became progressively fewer. The impoverishment of the European flora is well illustrated by the extinction of trees such as hickory (*Carya*), tulip tree (*Liriodendron*), *Magnolia* and hemlock (*Tsuga*), all of which survived in eastern North America. Similarly, walnut (*Juglans*) and the related *Pterocarya* disappeared from the region. The walnut now survives in south-eastern Europe while the nearest *Pterocarya* are in Iran. The reason why temperate floras in North America and Asia are much richer than the European is probably that there were no east-west mountain ranges to hinder the north-south migration of plants during the glaciations.

As the climate improved at the end of the last glaciation, the ice melted to expose bare, often stony, ground which was rich in unweathered minerals and plant nutrients. These open, base-rich soils were colonized by a wide range of tundra plants, particularly the dwarf birch (*Betula nana*) and calcicoles such as mountain avens (*Dryas octopetala*). This phase is known as the Late-glacial period.

It was succeeded by the Post-glacial period as the first trees, birch and Scots pine (*Pinus sylvestris*), gradually migrated into the area, probably from the east, producing forests similar to those existing today in northern Fennoscandia. (The term 'Fennoscandia' is used throughout when the area referred to includes Finland as well as the three Scandinavian countries, Denmark, Norway and Sweden.) About 8000 BC there was a rapid improvement in the climate, accompanied by a noticeable increase in the range of hazel (*Corylus avellana*), and followed by warmth-demanding trees, especially oak (*Quercus* species) and elm (*Ulmus* species). These probably invaded from the south-east but there is virtually no firm evidence of their origin. Other trees followed, notably alder (*Alnus glutinosa*), small-leaved lime (*Tilia cordata*) and Norway spruce (*Picea abies*). The result was that deciduous mixed-oak forest gradually replaced birch and pine forest, except in the mountains, the north and on poor, sandy soils. Furthermore, pine was displaced by

About six thousand years ago most of the lowlands of north-west Europe were covered with forest. This forest at Fontainebleau illustrates the way in which trees would have covered the whole landscape, with oak (*Quercus robur*), beech (*Fagus sylvatica*) and other trees even overhanging the edge of the Seine. The tree canopy is uneven, with some trees projecting well above the general level.

Right: Over the last two thousand years the climate has become colder and wetter and, in the west, vast areas of bogs have developed, blanketing the landscape. In many places peat cutting has removed the accumulated remains of the bog plants and here, in Ireland, has exposed the stumps of pine trees that grew in the earlier, drier conditions, before the blanket of peat developed.

spruce over large areas of eastern Fennoscandia. At a later stage, beech *(Fagus sylvatica)* and hornbeam *(Carpinus betulus)* replaced the oak forests on many of the drier, warmer calcareous soils and, on the European mainland, on the lower slopes of mountains. From 5000 to 3000 BC most of the lowlands in north-west Europe were covered by trees, the chief exceptions being maritime habitats and mires.

This picture, however, was soon to change. At about this time Neolithic man reached north-west Europe and immediately started to modify the natural vegetation. Unlike his hunting predecessors, he was an agriculturalist who cut down trees to increase the area for pasture, used trees such as elm as fodder for animals and created clearings in the forest where crops could be sown. At first, such agricultural activities were largely confined to dry, sandy areas, with the result that soil nutrients were soon exhausted. New clearings were therefore established. The older, abandoned clearings were either colonized by grasses, if grazed, or else reverted to scrub or woodland. As time passed, forests were cleared on an ever larger scale as human colonization spread and farming became increasingly intensive.

The warm, relatively dry climate of the major forest expansion did not last and around 500 BC colder and wetter conditions forced more warmth-demanding trees to lower altitudes or towards the south. The result of this change, coupled with deforestation, was that many of the high altitude woodlands in the oceanic parts of the region, and particularly in the British Isles, were replaced by a cover of blanket peat.

Deforestation has continued into the present century and has been accentuated over the last century and a half by ever-increasing industrialization and urbanization. In Britain alone the tree cover, once almost complete, has fallen to a mere 9 per cent and a substantial part of this consists of commercial coniferous plantations. As woodlands have been destroyed, grasslands have increased; in fact, throughout most of the region, practically all the lowland grasslands are man-made and it is now almost impossible to find any lowland, inland habitat which has not been, to a greater or lesser extent, influenced by man.

We begin our survey, therefore, by looking at what were originally the two major habitats—deciduous and coniferous forests—and then at their largely artificial derivatives, grasslands, heaths and moorland. This is followed by a description of mountain vegetation and a variety of aquatic and coastal habitats. The botanical compensations of an industrial landscape are discussed in Chapter 12 but the subject of the concluding chapter is inevitably a depressing one dealing, as it does, with the ever-increasing destruction and impoverishment of virtually every kind of natural and semi-natural habitat.

2
Deciduous forests and their flowers

This chapter is devoted to the woodlands and forests which, when mature, are composed predominantly of such familiar trees as beech *(Fagus sylvatica)*, hornbeam *(Carpinus betulus)*, species of oak *(Quercus)*, elm *(Ulmus)* and maple *(Acer)* and which lie scattered among the farmlands and pastures of the northern half of France, the lowland parts of the British Isles, the Low Countries, western Germany, Denmark, the southernmost part of Sweden and the German plain as far east as the middle Elbe. These constitute the deciduous forest zone of Europe from which Norway spruce *(Picea abies)*, although extensively planted, is absent as a native species, and Scots pine *(Pinus sylvestris)* occurs spontaneously or has become re-established, especially on sandy soils. To the north, on the coast of Norway and in southern Sweden and Finland, there is a zone of mixed deciduous forests, in which oak and elm are mixed with spruce and pine. This forms a transition to the northern (boreal) forests where deciduous species such as birch *(Betula* species), grey alder *(Alnus incana)* and aspen *(Populus tremula)*, are fairly common if the forest has been disturbed, but are always subordinate to coniferous trees in mature forest. East of the Elbe mixed forests of pine and oak occupy extensive areas of sandy soils, and yet farther east, in Poland, spruce is a natural constituent of the otherwise deciduous forests of oak and hornbeam.

The part of Europe in which typical summer-green deciduous forest occurs is characterized by moderate to fairly high rainfall (500–1500 mm per year) which is more or less evenly distributed throughout the year. The leafless period, lasting from four to six months, is determined by low temperatures, but neither winter nor summer temperatures are extreme. The mean temperature of the coldest months is usually not below −5°C and of the warmest, usually not above 20°C. From west to east, as has been mentioned, there is a marked change from a strongly oceanic to a more continental climate. It is probably this which is responsible

Beechwoods are amongst the grandest woodlands in our region. Beech *(Fagus sylvatica)* is one of the most tolerant trees of soil conditions, being equally at home on shallow alkaline soils over chalk as on acid, nutrient-poor sands.

for the different eastern and western limits of the natural distribution of the various tree species, so that the western limit of the elm *Ulmus laevis*, for example, is in eastern France, of hornbeam, England, of small-leaved lime *(Tilia cordata)*, Wales and of the oaks *Quercus robur* and *Q. petraea*, Ireland. Interestingly, the two evergreen trees which belong to the deciduous forest zone, holly *(Ilex aquifolium)* and yew *(Taxus baccata)*, both grow in the more western parts of the region, with the yew also around the Baltic.

The history of the forests

Our understanding of how woodlands have developed and of the variation which now exists in their structure and composition has been greatly helped by knowledge of their history. The main source of information is pollen preserved in the successive layers of sediment or peat in lakes and bogs. This can be extracted and identified, allowing the nature of the surrounding vegetation at the time the pollen was deposited to be reconstructed. In many sites the record starts during the closing phases of the last glaciation, about 20,000 years ago, and sometimes continues without interruption to the present day. Many sites scattered through the deciduous forest zone have now been studied and they show the northward spread of forest over the treeless hills and plains as temperatures rose after the Ice Age. At first the forests were composed of pine and birch but after 6500 BC these were gradually replaced by oak, elm and lime on the better-drained soils and by alder on wet soils beside rivers and lakes. By 5000 BC these species formed an almost continuous cover of trees over the whole of the present deciduous forest zone. At that period beech and hornbeam were restricted to the southern part of the zone, from which they subsequently spread northwards and westwards. It is difficult to judge to what extent this late expansion was a purely natural process because it coincides with increasing evidence of human activities, shown first by the appearance of pollen of weeds and cereal crops, sometimes associated with bands of charcoal, and then by an ever increasing proportion of the pollen of grasses, as forests were cleared and pastures established. There can be little doubt from the evidence available that in the absence of man most of the deciduous forest zone would still be thickly wooded. This is borne out by the rapidity with which trees, particularly oak and, in the oceanic areas, ash, invade abandoned pastures and arable fields so that forest reasserts itself within less than a century. Since the Middle Ages, at least, the pollen analytical record is supplemented by extensive documentary records consisting of inventories of standing timber, sales of timber, legislation for the preservation of forests and reports of how particular areas of woodland were treated.

From the mass of detailed historical information several facts of general relevance emerge. Firstly, it is clear that almost all woodlands within the deciduous forest zone have to a greater or lesser extent been influenced by man; probably no virgin deciduous forest now exists, apart from small and almost inaccessible fragments on cliffs and in narrow ravines which cannot be regarded as representative of the widespread forests of the past. Secondly, the structure of most woodlands and the proportions of species they contain are largely the products of human intervention. In spite of the scale of these modifications, many woods still consist almost entirely of native species whose natural distributions are now known with some certainty. Since at least the Roman period man has been responsible for extending the ranges of many species including the introduction of sweet chestnut *(Castanea sativa)* to northern France and Britain, and the introduction of sycamore *(Acer pseudoplatanus)* to Britain during the Middle Ages.

The amount of deciduous woodland composed of native species which exists today varies widely in different parts of the zone. Ireland has lost almost all its native woodlands; England, the Netherlands and Denmark retain only a small percentage, while France and Germany still have a substantial proportion of their total area wooded, 25 per cent and 30 per cent respectively. If we accept the historical evidence that almost all agricultural land has been derived

The deciduous forests of Fennoscandia are often full of wild flowers. Between the trees and bushes of juniper *(Juniperus communis)* of this Finnish wood are yellow cowslips *(Primula veris)*, taller, pink wood cranesbill *(Geranium sylvaticum)*, dark red and pale yellow spikes of the orchid *Dactylorhiza sambucina* and, here and there, the bright yellow flowers of buttercups *(Ranunculus* species). Peak flowering period May-June.

The lesser celandine *(Ranunculus ficaria)* is a common flower of woods, meadows, grassy banks and streamsides. It is easily recognized by its three sepals, 8-12 yellow petals and its rosette of heart-shaped leaves. Flowering period: March-May.

from forest (arable land often from oak forest and pastures from beech forest) then the small amounts of forest which remain reflect the extent of human activity.

The woodland trees

By comparison with the temperate parts of either North America or eastern Asia, Europe has remarkably few native deciduous trees; not more than a dozen species play a significant role in the deciduous forests. Reduced to its simplest level, the relation between the main types of woodland is determined by the proportion of beech to other species, particularly oaks. The distribution of beech is clearly correlated with climate: it does not grow in regions with severe winter cold or pronounced summer drought. As a result it occurs only sparsely over the German plain but forms extensive forests on the hills of western Germany, where the rainfall is higher. In Belgium and eastern France beech replaces oak at altitudes above 450–500m where rainfall exceeds 1000mm and is rare or absent from the dry regions of Beauce and the middle Loire. In the oceanic climate of Normandy and in southern England, a relation to altitude is scarcely discernible and human influence is often decisive in determining whether the dominant species is oak or beech. Within those regions where the climate is favourable to beech, it grows on calcareous, neutral and acid soils, but is intolerant of waterlogged and poorly aerated soils. Where beech thrives, its height, the deep shade that it casts, the tolerance of its shade by its own seedlings and its dense but shallow roots make it a vigorous and persistent competitor so that it can exclude most other species, including oak.

In regions of low rainfall (less than 600–700mm per year) and with warm summers and cold winters, oak and hornbeam seem to have a clear advantage over beech, which becomes less common or is entirely absent. Sessile oak *(Quercus petraea)* tends to occur on better-drained soils, including, as its Latin name indicates, rocky sites, and it extends into the most oceanic parts of both Brittany and the British Isles, from which beech and hornbeam are absent. Pedunculate oak *(Q. robur)* favours heavy soils which are often poorly aerated, especially in winter. Such soils are in themselves unfavourable for beech, so that oak-hornbeam or oak-ash woods usually occupy them even within the climatic zone where otherwise beech might be successful. It must be remembered that many sites of this type have been improved by drainage, further affecting natural distribution.

Prolonged or permanent waterlogging of the soil excludes all the species which have been mentioned so far and it is in these conditions that alder *(Alnus glutinosa)* and willows *(Salix* species) thrive.

Beech forest

Forests of beech are widespread on the hills of western Germany, the Ardenne, Luxembourg and north-eastern France, with smaller, more scattered areas farther west in France and southern England and farther north on the Baltic coast of Germany, Denmark and southern Sweden. Beech is one of the most valuable European hardwood timbers and is normally grown as high forest, with the trees allowed to grow as straight as possible and to their fullest height. Wherever possible it is regenerated naturally from seedlings by clear or successive fellings. It can also be coppiced, that is cut close to the ground, but the stumps often sprout weakly and the stools they form easily become infected by fungi and decay. Because beech timber is so valuable, the absence or scarcity of other trees is often the result of forestry practices, such as 'weeding', rather than simply their elimination by competition.

Variation in the quality of beech is closely related to the depth, fertility and chemical conditions of the soil which also to a large extent determine the nature of the ground flora. On shallow calcareous soils the trees are stunted, rarely over 22–25m tall and often with curved trunks, and they grow associated with common whitebeam (*Sorbus aria*) and yew. The shallow roots of the beech may exploit the soil so effectively that almost all herbaceous species are excluded and the bareness of beech forests is often more a result of root competition than of shade. White helleborine (*Cephalanthera damasonium*), sanicle (*Sanicula europaea*) and the sedge *Carex flacca* are among the few species which will tolerate such extreme conditions. They are replaced by extensive patches of dog's-mercury (*Mercurialis perennis*) on deeper calcareous soils, and ash (*Fraxinus excelsior*) is generally plentiful in the more open parts of the forest.

The finest quality beech, perhaps 30m tall and with straight cylindrical trunks, is found on deep, brown forest soils. On such soils dead leaves tend to disappear quite rapidly and not to accumulate on the surface. The underlying mineral material is crumbly, at least near the surface, because it is well worked by earthworms, and it has a uniform greyish-brown colour to a depth of 50–100cm. In beech woods on this type of soil sessile oak may be present, and sycamore, Norway maple (*Acer platanoides*) and ash may persist, at least in gaps. The herbaceous vegetation varies according to the fertility and depth of the soil. On the best sites it usually includes woodruff (*Galium odoratum*), the grasses *Melica uniflora* and *Milium effusum*, wood anemone (*Anemone nemorosa*), yellow archangel (*Lamiastrum galeobdolon*), hairy wood-rush (*Luzula pilosa*) and the ferns *Dryopteris dilatata* and *D. filix-mas*. In shallow valleys where the soil is damper and beside streams, ramsons (*Allium*

ursinum) is often so abundant as to exclude almost all other herbs. On rather more acid soils, wood sorrel (*Oxalis acetosella*) is characteristic, and, where the soil is shallower, wood fescue *Festuca altissima* may be dominant. With even more marked soil acidity, the wood-rush *Luzula nemorosa* is widespread in the more continental beech forests, while bluebell (*Hyacinthoides non-scripta*) is a feature of the oceanic ones.

The most acid soils show podzolic features: beneath the layer of dead beech leaves the older leaves are incompletely decayed and lie matted together by white fungal mycelium and mycorrhiza (fungal roots), separated from the brown crumbly loam beneath by a compact layer of pale grey loam, often flecked with rusty marks. Such a soil is transitional

Left: The interior of a beech wood is often very bare, with few or no species growing beneath the trees. The main reasons are the dense shade cast by the canopy and the very shallow rooting system which uses up all the water and nutrients in the top layers of the soil. The dead leaves are slow to decay and so smother any germinating seeds. Such woods harbour the bird's nest orchid *(Neottia nidus-avis)*, which has no chlorophyll and obtains its food from decaying material.

Ramsons *(Allium ursinum)* can form extensive carpets in woods that have very moist soils, particularly those at the bottom of slopes or along riversides. Flowering period: April-June.

Left: The wood anemone *(Anemone nemorosa)*, a member of the buttercup family, is one of the commonest flowers of oak or beech woods on moist, rich brown forest soils. Whole woods may be carpeted with its delicate, white flowers. Like many woodland herbs, it has an underground rhizome from which shoots arise in early spring and by June, when the trees are in full leaf, hardly a trace remains. Flowering period: March-May.

The snowdrop *(Galanthus nivalis)* grows wild in damp woods and shady streamsides in the southern part of the region. Its northern limits have been obscured by extensive planting and naturalization, so that it is not certain whether it is native north of France and Germany. Flowering period: January-March.

Like wood anemones, bluebells *(Hyacinthoides non-scripta)* are only visible above ground in spring and early summer. In mainland Europe they grow only in the extreme west, where they are characteristic of oak woods on the more acidic soils. Flowering period: April-early June.

Forest soil types

1 Brown forest soil is crumbly and more or less uniformly grey-brown in colour, With depth, the colour usually lightens as there are more rock fragments. Little or no organic debris accumulates at the surface, largely because it is quickly incorporated into the soil by earthworms and other animals.

2 Soil in the early stages of podzolization. There is an accumulation of litter at the surface, below which is a compact layer of pale grey loam, often with rusty marks, and, lower still, brown crumbly loam.

3 Podzol. Partly decomposed dead leaves have accumulated at the surface above a layer of almost pure acidic humus resting on a white sand. Almost all the iron oxide has been removed from this sand and some is re-deposited as a dark brown, hard layer, the iron pan. Below this is a relatively unaltered soil with dark lines representing the root channels of former trees.

Bastard balm (*Melittis melissophyllum*) is a tall, striking plant rather like an extra large dead-nettle. It grows in the south of the region, particularly in dry open woodlands of *Quercus pubescens* on sunny, south-facing slopes. Flowering period: May-July.

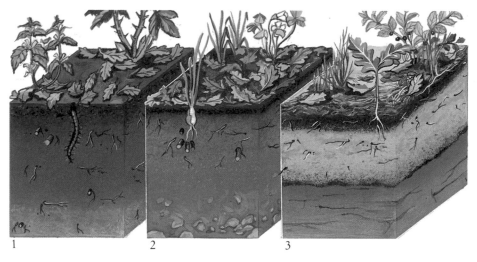

1   2   3

between a brown forest soil and a true podzol, in which the upper mineral layer (corresponding to the pale grey loam layer of the podzolic soil) is a white sand from which almost all iron oxide has been dissolved. The iron oxide is redeposited to form a hard layer known as an iron pan.

The trees that grow on podzolic soils are of poor quality and rarely exceed 23–25 m in height; regeneration may fail even though there are often numerous saplings which are held in check. The ground-layer is dominated by wavy hair-grass (*Deschampsia flexuosa*) and bilberry (*Vaccinium myrtillus*).

Forests in ravines and on steep slopes

Among hills and low mountains, especially in France and western Germany, where beech forests are common on the plateaux and slopes, fragments of another type of forest often survive on cliffs and ravines. Because they are difficult to reach and of poor quality, they have escaped exploitation, and there is therefore some justification for regarding this type of forest as primitive. On north-facing sites and in narrow ravines the forest remains in shadow throughout the greater part of the day and the air stays cool and humid. There is often shelter from wind and protection by deep accumulation of snow in winter. Although beech is nearly always present, the trees are misshapen and stunted, growing mixed with sessile oak, sycamore, Norway maple, wych elm (*Ulmus glabra*) and large-leaved lime (*Tilia platyphyllos*). The trunks of the trees and rocks are covered by mosses in which ferns and particularly hart's-tongue (*Phyllitis scolopendrium*) and hard shield-fern (*Polystichum aculeatum*), are rooted.

In contrast, south-facing sites may act as sun-traps and provide congenial conditions for species whose main distribution is in southern Europe.. Where the slope is steep and the soil shallow, south-facing sites tend to become dry and warm during the summer. This, combined with a shortage of mineral nutrients (particularly nitrogen and phosphorus) gives the vegetation a very distinctive appearance. The tree canopy and, indeed, plant cover in general is sparse. Both trees and shrubs are stunted and the leaves often develop rather intense red and orange colours, especially in autumn. On sunny days, even in winter, the warmth in the glades is striking and the whole atmosphere is redolent of southern Europe.

Sites of this type occur as far north as southern England, where, for example, on the steep slopes of white chalk at Box Hill in Surrey, undercut by the river Mole, box (*Buxus sempervirens*), common whitebeam and yew combine to give a type of vegetation which is reminiscent of the limestone

The purple gromwell *(Buglossoides purpurocaerulea)* is another plant of sunny, south-facing slopes. Flowering period: May-July.

Left: In an agricultural economy, woods were managed to provide timber for the community. Tall, straight standards, here oak *(Quercus robur)*, provided the major construction timber while the many straight stems growing from the coppiced hazel *(Corylus avellana)* were harvested at regular intervals and used for a variety of purposes. The ground is covered by wood anemones.

regions of southern France. Similar sites occur along the Seine and Meuse. One of the most characteristic trees of such situations in France and the Rhine valley is the small oak *Quercus pubescens*. It seems to be even more drought resistant than the two common oaks; at least in its natural habitats, it rarely grows to more than 15m in height and is usually little more than half that. Belgium and France form its northern limit but it shuns the coastal districts. A notable feature of the woodland, or more often scrub, where *Quercus pubescens* grows is the wealth of woody species, which often number more than ten and sometimes as many as twenty. This is again reminiscent of southern Europe. The broken canopy allows more sunlight through and many herbaceous species, some no less characteristic of grassland, persist. Among the most characteristic trees and shrubs are the maples *Acer campestre* and *A. opulus*, buckthorn *(Rhamnus catharticus)*, wayfaring tree *(Viburnum lantana)*, wild privet *(Ligustrum vulgare)*, a small cherry *Prunus mahaleb*, service-tree *(Sorbus domestica)*, the dogwoods *Cornus mas* and *C. sanguinea* and barberry *(Berberis vulgaris)*, as well as the more widespread spiny shrubs, hawthorn *(Crataegus monogyna)* and blackthorn *(Prunus spinosa)*. The herbaceous vegetation is also so varied that a representative list would be very long, but among the most striking species are the delicate lily *Anthericum ramosum*, an asclepiad *Vincetoxicum hirundinaria*, purple gromwell *Buglossoides purpurocaerulea*, bastard balm *(Melittis melissophyllum* and the sickle-leaved hare's-ear *(Bupleurum falcatum)*.

Oak, oak-hornbeam and oak-ash woods

Throughout the historic period oak has been the most esteemed of the native hardwoods of Europe. Well-grown timber has always been valued for its strength and durability, being used extensively for buildings and by maritime nations for the construction of ships. Both sessile and pedunculate oak can be coppiced and their stools persist for many centuries, providing regular crops of poles which are suitable for firewood or the manufacture of charcoal, as well as bark for tanning. The heavy crops of acorns were an important source of feed for pigs.

Oaks may grow to 30m on the best sites but they cast a lighter shade than beech; they are deep rooted and this contributes to their tolerance of drought, but also means that competition from their roots in the upper part of the soil is less severe. Oak seedlings are intolerant of deep shade but will grow successfully under a light canopy when the forest is thinned. For this reason oak regenerates poorly or fails to regenerate in the deep shade under coppice, whether of oak itself or some other species.

Many fine stands of oak which still exist in France were produced by a once traditional but now discontinued system of regeneration known as *tire et aire*, whereby adjacent patches of about 5–7 ha were cut at one time, leaving 15 to 20 mature trees per hectare. Under such conditions oak regenerates freely and with careful thinning gives tall, straight trees which are mature at about one hundred years.

This has been replaced by the 'uniform' system which is now widely used for oak in both France and Germany. It is most simply described from the stage when a final crop of trees, all of the same age, is mature and forms an unbroken canopy. Felling proceeds in a succession of cuts made over a period of up to 10 to 15 years. The first removes perhaps half the number of trees and by opening the canopy promotes establishment of a dense population of seedlings (5–10,000 per ha). When this is achieved then more of the parent trees are removed to encourage the growth of the new generation and finally, when these attain a height of about 2 m, the remaining old trees are cut. The new generation is therefore uniform in age and as it grows taller, poorly grown oaks and other species, such as birch, aspen, hornbeam and lime are cut out, leaving a dense growth of saplings which are thinned gradually to encourage the production of tall, straight, unbranched stems and a final density of 200–300 per ha.

In many forests throughout Europe, oaks used to be grown widely spaced as standards at densities sometimes as low as 30 per ha. This allowed the vigorous growth of an understorey of hornbeam, hazel (*Corylus avellana*) or small-leaved lime, which was cut at frequent intervals very close to the ground to form coppice. Woods of this type, known as coppice-with-standards, are scattered throughout the agricultural landscape and their main function was to provide fuel and timber for local needs. Many were still treated in the traditional way until after the first world war, but within a generation the whole pattern of rural economy of which they

The common violet (*Viola riviniana*) grows in a wide variety of habitats and in woodland is usually confined to richer soils. It is growing here with the round leaves of navelwort (*Umbilicus rupestris*) and the palmate leaves of creeping cinquefoil (*Potentilla reptans*). Flowering period: May-June.

Top: *Corydalis solida* is quite common in mainland Europe in woods on moist brown forest soil or calcareous soils. Here it is growing with dogs mercury (*Mercurialis perennis*). Flowering period: March-May.

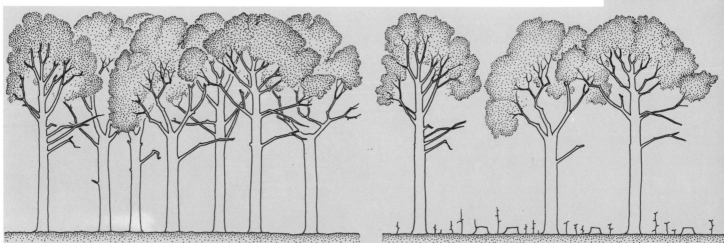

1

2

formed a part disappeared. In France coppice-with-standards has been retained in many communal forests, but most state forests, including the great royal hunting forests which passed to the state after the Revolution, have now been converted to high forest, in which all the trees are standards.

Oak forests are characteristic of low altitudes, below 350–400m, and of regions of relatively low rainfall. These are, of course, the most intensively farmed parts of the deciduous forest zone and now that the woodlands have lost their original purpose there is a strong temptation to clear them and cultivate the land. Many of the surviving woodlands occupy sites which have certainly been wooded since the Middle Ages and probably for much longer. They must surely represent the much modified remnants of the original prehistoric mixed oak forest which once covered the whole zone but, as pollen analysis shows, the proportions of species seem to have been drastically changed. Elm and small-leaved lime have diminished, in some areas almost to extinction, while ash and hornbeam and probably hazel have greatly

increased because their small timbers are so useful for a wide variety of agricultural and domestic purposes.

Oak woods occur on a wide variety of soils ranging from calcareous to strongly acid, (as do beech woods) but also from those which are well drained to those which are poorly drained, so that standards of oak may have ash or even alder forming the underwood. Such a wide range of soils is associated with a considerable variety of herbaceous vegetation. Calcareous and neutral soils with moderate drainage are characterized by a mixture of herbs in which the following are often conspicuous: wood anemone, the violets *Viola reichenbachiana* and *V. riviniana*, wood spurge (*Euphorbia amygdaloides*), lungwort (*Pulmonaria obscura*), dog's mercury, ground-elder (*Aegopodium podagraria*), enchanter's-nightshade (*Circaea lutetiana*), early-purple orchid (*Orchis mascula*), herb-paris (*Paris quadrifolia*), Solomon's-seal (*Polygonatum multiflorum*) and the grass *Brachypodium sylvaticum*.

The best quality oaks grow on deep, well-drained, mildly

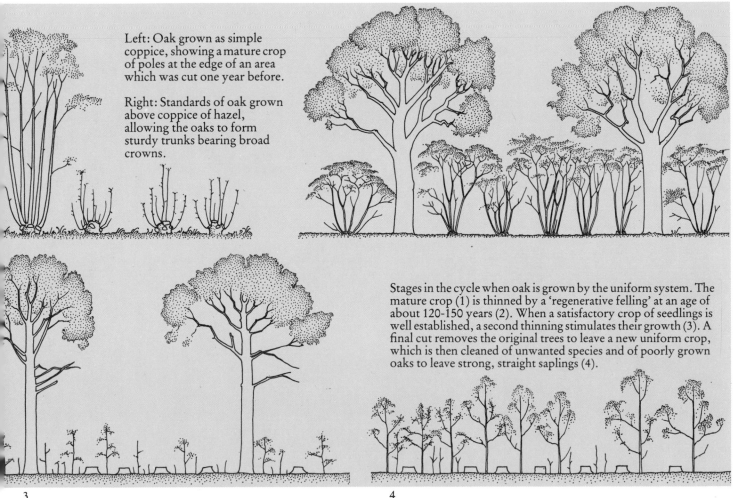

Left: Oak grown as simple coppice, showing a mature crop of poles at the edge of an area which was cut one year before.

Right: Standards of oak grown above coppice of hazel, allowing the oaks to form sturdy trunks bearing broad crowns.

Stages in the cycle when oak is grown by the uniform system. The mature crop (1) is thinned by a 'regenerative felling' at an age of about 120-150 years (2). When a satisfactory crop of seedlings is well established, a second thinning stimulates their growth (3). A final cut removes the original trees to leave a new uniform crop, which is then cleaned of unwanted species and of poorly grown oaks to leave strong, straight saplings (4).

3

4

The lungwort *Pulmonaria officinalis*, with its white-blotched leaves said to resemble lungs, is a member of the borage family. The flower changes from pink to blue with age. To find this plant, look in the warmer, drier woods of mainland Europe, particularly on calcareous soils. Flowering period: March-May.

Far left: Herb Paris *(Paris quadrifolia)* is easily recognized by its whorl of four leaves and stem topped by a single flower. Usually the flower has four green sepals and four pale, very narrow petals. It is found in woods on calcareous soils. Flowering period: May-August.

Left: The Solomon's seal *(Polygonatum multiflorum)* is a characteristic plant of oak woods on calcareous or brown forest soils. Its graceful, arching stems grow from a thick, creeping rhizome, and its small, cylindrical flowers are in groups of two to five. Its close relative *P. odoratum* has somewhat larger flowers which grow singly or in pairs. Flowering season: May-June.

acid, but fertile brown forest soils, characterized by a field-layer composed of wood anemone, common dog-violet *(Viola riviniana)*, greater stitchwort *(Stellaria holostea)*, yellow archangel and wood millet *(Milium effusum)*. The bedstraw *Galium sylvaticum* is found in this type of woodland on the north German plain, while bluebell, primrose *(Primula vulgaris)* and wild daffodil *(Narcissus pseudonarcissus)* occur, often in great profusion, in Belgium, western France and England.

With increasing acidity of the soil, the grass *Holcus mollis* and bracken *(Pteridium aquilinum)* become widespread, and in the more oceanic areas holly often forms an understorey beneath the oaks while honeysuckle *(Lonicera periclymenum)* is common. It is in these conditions that bluebell can almost dominate the field-layer, providing one of the most beautiful features of European woodland. On very steep slopes, where there is no grazing, large tufts of great wood-rush *(Luzula sylvatica)* may be so dominant as to exclude all other herbs. The most acid soils support wavy hair-grass and bilberry, which are associated, as they are in beech woods, with podzolization. It is in this type of woodland in Brittany and the westernmost parts of the British Isles that there is sometimes an extraordinary luxuriance of mosses and liverworts, many of which are only found in these extremely oceanic areas. They form a thick green carpet over the boulders, fallen logs and bases of the trunks, while the polypody fern *(Polypodium vulgare)* and wood sorrel grow on the limbs of the trees and large lichens festoon the branches. The strawberry-tree *(Arbutus unedo)* grows in this type of woodland in south-western Ireland and in Brittany, although its main distribution is in the *maquis* of the Mediterranean region.

These western woodlands were formerly exploited for charcoal and bark for tanning, but are now derelict. Often the boundary walls have collapsed and they are grazed by sheep, so that oak fails to regenerate and as the old trees die they are replaced perhaps by birch, but often just by bracken.

Wet oak woods

A very different type of oak woodland is to be found on heavy clays in northern France, parts of southern England and the English Midlands. Some of these woodlands are of great antiquity, but many occupy lands that were formerly cultivated and still bear the unmistakable signs of ridge-and-furrow. In the wet climate of western Europe claylands have always been intractable. Ploughing with horses is extremely difficult so that in times of depression the fields were often abandoned. They were colonized quite rapidly, at first by hawthorn and then, because the hawthorn provided

Primroses *(Primula vulgaris)* grow in woods in the west of the region, on rich brown forest soils. In the extreme west they may grow on hedgebanks or grasslands even growing with thrift and sea campion on sea cliffs. Flowering period: December-May.

Left; Honeysuckle *(Lonicera periclymenum)* is found in woods, hedges, scrub or even scrambling over rocks, usually on neutral or rather acid soils. Its flowers are adapted for pollination by larger moths, though bumble-bees visit them as well. Flowering period: June-September.

protection from grazing cattle, by oak and ash. Such woodlands are witness to the fluctuating fortunes of agriculture.

Pedunculate oak and ash are both remarkably tolerant of soils which are poorly drained and poorly aerated, so that they tend to dominate woodlands on compact clays where water may actually stand on the surface during most winters. They often grow together with elms, including *Ulmus procera* and *U. minor*, and *U. laevis* in the more continental areas. It is these elms which are so stricken with Dutch elm disease. Old woodlands are marked by the presence of the woodland hawthorn *Crataegus laevigata*, while newer woodlands retain the common hawthorn for at least a century. The ground may remain so wet even in summer that the herbaceous layer is like that of a fen, with meadowsweet *(Filipendula ulmaria)* and sedges. Ash becomes dominant where springs emerge and the sodden clay around them is occupied by large tussocks of the sedge *Carex pendula* and the great horsetail *Equisetum telmateia*. In northern France, Belgium and East Anglia, oxlip *(Primula elatior)* may dominate the field-layer in this type of woodland, indicating that the clay is calcareous. On acid clays a herbaceous layer dominated by purple moor-grass *(Molinia caerulea)* is a widespread feature of northern France but seems to be almost absent from England.

Wild daffodils *(Narcissus pseudonarcissus)* are really only found in profusion in the southern parts of the region but have been widely introduced elsewhere. They grow in oakwoods on moist, well drained brown forest soil. Flowering period: February–April.

Butterbur *(Petasites hybridus)* is a plant of wet woodlands and streamsides. It flowers before the leaves appear but the leaves soon grow very large, up to 90cm across, looking rather like very hairy rhubarb leaves. Flowering period: March–May.

Alder and willow woods

Alder and most willows, including the crack willow *(Salix fragilis)*, the sallow or grey willow *(S. cinerea)*, and the osiers *S. viminalis, S. purpurea* and *S. triandra*, not only require a plentiful supply of water, but can grow healthily with their roots in soils where the water-table is at, or above, the surface, either permanently or for much of the year. Osiers and crack willow normally fringe rivers, occupying the levées, areas where fresh sediment is deposited whenever the river floods and overflows its banks. They are dependent on this sediment for mineral nutrients and when a river changes its course and the supply is cut off, the osier beds languish and soon become moribund. The fertility of the soil in osier beds is reflected in the luxuriance of their herbaceous vegetation, which is usually composed of the reed-like grass *Phalaris arundinacea*, nettle *(Urtica dioica)*, meadowsweet, hedge woundwort *(Stachys sylvatica)*, common comfrey *(Symphytum officinale)* and hop *(Humulus lupulus)*. In the natural state osier beds are relatively transient communities, establishing themselves on banks of bare shingle and mud formed by a river, only to die out as the river moves away. The minute seedlings of willows require bare ground and there is no regeneration under either the parent trees or among the lush herbaceous vegetation.

In contrast, alder and grey willow are much more persistent. Their seedlings also require bare ground but the trees live longer and, although they thrive on fertile alluvium, they will also grow where water stagnates, so that they will occupy the depressions of the flood plain behind the levées and even isolated hollows where no sediment is deposited.

On fertile alluvial soils, where the water-level falls in summer, pedunculate oak, ash and elms are associated with alder to form a type of forest which now exists only in fragments but must once have been widespread on the flood plains of the larger rivers. In well-lit parts, the herbaceous vegetation includes the same tall species that are common in osier beds, but where there is deeper summer shade, wood anemone, lesser celandine *(Ranunculus ficaria)* and patches of moschatel *(Adoxa moschatellina)* carpet the ground in spring, to be followed by wild garlic *(Allium* species) and ground-elder. The agricultural value of such situations has

Left: In the extreme west, where summer temperatures are low and the atmosphere is humid, exposed oak woods on poor acid soil and rocky hill slopes are full of poorly grown, misshapen trees. They and the rocks beneath are covered by a luxuriance of mosses, liverworts, lichens and ferns, many species of which are confined to the oceanic fringes of our region. Here moss-covered sessile oaks (*Quercus petraea*) have an understorey of bracken.

The guelder rose (*Viburnum opulus*) is a small shrub growing to 4m high in damp woods. The outer flowers are sterile and merely serve to attract pollinators. The inner flowers are replaced in autumn by bright red fruits. Flowering period: June-July.

Calla palustris is a member of the arum family and grows in the wettest, muddiest places in alder woods and on pond or river banks. Flowering period: June-July.

long been recognized and their woodland has been cleared to be replaced by fertile meadows and rich pastures.

Alder is generally the only tree which will grow in the standing water of the wettest sites. On fertile soil large bitter-cress (*Cardamine amara*), marsh-marigold (*Caltha palustris*), golden saxifrages (*Chrysosplenium alternifolium* and *C. oppositifolium*) and the white aroid, *Calla palustris*, grow in the liquid mud and rivulets; ferns, particularly the buckler ferns *Dryopteris carthusiana* and *D. dilatata* and the royal fern (*Osmunda regalis*), grow on rotting logs or on the sides of large tussocks of the sedge *Carex paniculata*. An abundance of the very poisonous hemlock water-dropwort (*Oenanthe crocata*) is a distinctive feature of western alder woods. But alder is by no means restricted to neutral waters and it forms woods in moorland valleys where the waters are acid, coloured brown with peat and deficient in dissolved minerals or sediment: in these situations it is usually found with downy birch (*Betula pubescens*). Bog mosses (*Sphagnum* species) grow between the tree bases, with tufts of purple moor-grass and, in western Europe, thickets of bog myrtle (*Myrica gale*). This small, fragrant-leaved shrub resembles alder in bearing nodules on its roots which are formed in association with a bacterium-like organism and are capable of fixing atmospheric nitrogen.

Many alder woods, though certainly not of great antiquity, probably possess a structure which is more truly natural than that of any other woodland. Though once exploited for charcoal, now, on sites too wet to drain, they are little disturbed either by humans or by domestic animals. With their fallen trees, rotting logs and luxuriant ferns surrounding stagnant pools, they retain an atmosphere of wilderness not easily sensed in any other type of woodland.

3
Coniferous forests
of the north

In the early Post-glacial period much of the central and western part of the region was occupied by forests of birch *(Betula* species) and of Scots pine *(Pinus sylvestris)*. With the final improvement in the climate just after the end of the Late-glacial period, these forests migrated northwards into Denmark and southern Sweden to colonize the more or less treeless tundra and they rapidly advanced over most of the rest of Fennoscandia, closely following the receding ice sheet. At about the same time the forests of pine were in turn displaced from most of western Europe by deciduous forest entering the area from southern France and central Europe.

The final result of these migrations and the much later invasion of Norway spruce *(Picea abies)* is that native coniferous forests have a restricted distribution in west-central Europe but cover very large areas north of the deciduous forest zone. This is the boreal coniferous zone which extends not only over most of Fennoscandia but continues in a broad belt eastwards through the Russian *taiga* and across northern North America.

The boundary between deciduous and coniferous forest is broad and the change from one type to the other is gradual. Transitional forests with warmth-demanding deciduous trees or stands of deciduous trees interspersed among the boreal coniferous forests occur in many parts of southern Norway and Sweden, and in southernmost Finland. South of the Baltic Sea, from the Dutch border eastwards, there are pine woods in the lowlands as well as in the uplands, but native spruce is more restricted, growing chiefly in the high hills near the south-eastern limit of the region. Finally, pine has survived in Scotland continuously since the early Post-glacial period and here, as well as in a few places in France and in most of western and northernmost Norway, there are native pine woods but no indigenous spruce.

Of the other north-west European conifers, the silver fir *(Abies alba)* grows locally in hills along the southern fringe of the region, mixed with beech *(Fagus sylvatica)* and also with

A spruce forest in eastern Finland. The ground flora consists largely of bog moss (*Sphagnum* species), cloudberry (*Rubus chamaemorus*) and bilberry (*Vaccinium myrtillus*). The dead branches of the trees are festooned with the lichen *Usnea*.

37

spruce. The yew *(Taxus baccata)* occurs as far north as western Norway and the Baltic coastal areas, including the Ahvenanmaa (Åland) islands of Finland. Juniper *(Juniperus communis)* is the only conifer which is common throughout the region. At best it forms scrub of varying height or even small trees, but never true forest. It needs plenty of light and grows best in treeless landscapes or open woodlands, dying off when taller trees close the canopy.

On the European mainland a subalpine zone of dwarfed spruce occurs within the region on the highest hills of the Harz. In Fennoscandia, however, a well-developed subalpine zone, dominated almost exclusively by a subspecies of downy birch *(Betula pubescens)*, extends above the coniferous forests to the tree-line. In the British Isles the tree-line has been lowered everywhere by grazing by both sheep and deer and also by burning. These two factors have for centuries prevented regeneration with the result that natural subalpine woods are poorly developed. Grazing particularly has similarly affected the once widespread Icelandic birchwoods. There are no coniferous forests in Iceland, the only indigenous conifer being juniper.

Pine forests

Native pine woods occur over nearly the whole of Fennoscandia although not in Denmark. In mainland Europe they are scattered roughly east of a line from the Netherlands-German border to the Jura but it is only farther east, for example on the north German plain, that they become a major feature of the landscape. The distribution of the native pine woods surviving in Scotland and France has been obscured not only by grazing and burning but by widespread commercial planting over the last 150 years.

One type of Fennoscandian pine wood occurs particularly in coastal areas. It has developed on ice-scoured rocks of granite and gneiss where soil is largely limited to fissures. Along the Baltic coast the windswept rocks and archipelagos have emerged only relatively recently from the sea as the land slowly recovers from the weight of the ice-sheet. These open rocky woodlands suffer from extreme drought in some summers and have only a sparse cover of ground plants. The bare rock is colonized first by crustaceous and foliaceous lichens. Eventually the moss *Rhacomitrium lanuginosum* may appear and later reindeer lichen *(Cladonia* species), spreading from the middle of the moss cushions, takes over. When dry, this is a very fragile covering and strong dry winds or trampling by moose or man can disrupt it, so starting the cycle of colonization again. In favourable seasons heather *(Calluna vulgaris)* may colonize the lichen-moss mats but when severe drought occurs it dies, surviving only in crevices where soil has accumulated.

Conifers can colonize very inhospitable habitats. On this Finnish island, there is very little soil amongst the ice-smoothed rocks, yet juniper *(Juniperus communis)* is growing well.

Right: Pine woods on well-drained sands and gravels are rich in lichens. This wood in central Sweden has a ground vegetation dominated by the lichen reindeer moss *(Cladonia alpestris)* and *Cetraria nivalis*. There is little else but the occasional dwarf shrub surrounding the massive ice-borne boulder.

Lichen-rich pine woods on well-drained gravels and sands such as eskers, deltas, outwash plains and former dunes, are widespread, especially in Fennoscandia. The soils are podzols (see page 28) and the flora is generally similar to that of the pine woods on rocky outcrops although the individual trees are much taller and closer together. However, they grow rather slowly and the productivity of such forests is low; their rotation period in commercial forestry often exceeds a century. Like the pine woods on rock, these woods have a poor ground flora, apart from lichens, the most conspicuous plants being heather, cowberry *(Vaccinium vitis-idaea)* and often bearberry *(Arctostaphylos uva-ursi)*. Largely because of the lichen cover, these forests, and also the lichen-rich subarctic birch woods at very high latitudes, are the main winter feeding grounds for the herds of semi-domesticated reindeer of northern Fennoscandia. Overgrazing and trampling may, in time, lead to the replacement of the *Cladonia* by the more resistant lichen *Stereocaulon*. Woods free from grazing have a very luxuriant lichen mat in which the tall, attractive *Cladonia alpestris* is conspicuous.

On slightly damper sites lichens are largely replaced by mosses, for example *Hylocomium splendens, Pleurozium schreberi* and species of *Dicranum*. Dwarf shrubs play a more prominent role, in particular cowberry, both subspecies of

The cowberry *(Vaccinium vitis-idaea)* is an evergreen dwarf shrub, closely related to heather. It has small, bell-like pinkish flowers and, in late summer or autumn, bright red edible berries. Cowberries are particularly characteristic of pine forests, but also occur on moors and in acid oak woods. Flowering period: June-August.

crowberry *(Empetrum nigrum)*, heather and bilberry *(Vaccinium myrtillus)*. Especially in richer pine woods, or woods that have been disturbed in the past, lily-of-the-valley *(Convallaria majalis)*, the tall grass *Calamagrostis arundinacea* and bracken *(Pteridium aquilinum)* may be prominent. Less common are the clubmoss *Lycopodium complanatum*, an early-flowering species of pasqueflower, *Pulsatilla vernalis*, the wintergreen *Pyrola chlorantha* and the related dwarf shrub *Chimaphila umbellata*. Although lacking nearly all these plants, similar but often moister pine woods occur widely in Scotland. In addition to heather, these are often characterized by an abundance of bilberry and occasionally by the creeping lady's-tresses orchid *(Goodyera repens)*, which in other areas is more typical of spruce woods. Most north German pine woods are similarly rich in bilberry and also wavy hair-grass *(Deschampsia flexuosa)*. The drier, lichen-rich woods are restricted to the poorest sands and feature broom *(Cytisus scoparius)* and various species of *Genista*. Farther west, pine increasingly gives way to pedunculate oak *(Quercus robur)* or birch, usually silver birch *(Betula pendula)*.

Pine woods also grow on limestone, for instance at a site just east of the Trondheim Fjord in Norway, where the ground flora includes mountain avens *(Dryas octopetala)* and other calcicoles; on the Baltic island of Gotland and in

Bearberry *(Arctostaphylos uva-ursi)* is a dwarf shrub with long, rooting branches which become so interwoven that they form a mat. The evergreen leaves have a conspicuous network of veins and the flowers are rather like those of cowberry, white tinged with pink. The round, red fruit ripen in the autumn. Flowering period: May-July.

southern Germany. These limestone pine woods have very different floras, containing many rare herbs and grasses. Of special interest in this respect are the rather open pine woods on the steep slopes of some glacial eskers and moraine ridges, found particularly in southern Finland.

Pine woods, however, are by no means restricted to well-drained sites but occur commonly on peatlands, where they either grow as a fringe around the edge or spread out across the surface of the bog.

Spruce forests

Native spruce has a more restricted and a more easterly distribution than pine. It is absent from the western part of the region and most of the north German plain but to the south it forms forests in the Harz and Thüringer Wald. Here it dominates the upper forest zone, usually above beech *(Fagus sylvatica)*. There are no native spruce woods in Denmark but they occur over most of the rest of Fennoscandia except on the southern and western coasts and in northern Norway. They are, however, common in Tröndelag and Nordland.

Spruce prefers moister soils than does pine and is more exacting in its nutrient requirements. Although it can compete successfully with pine on moist soils, it cannot oust pine from the poorer or drier soils. These factors, as well as the history and management of the forests (their thinning, cutting, grazing, burnbeating and forest fires) combine to determine the relative distributions of the two dominant trees in coniferous forests in Fennoscandia.

Spruce casts a deeper shade than pine. The soil under both is usually of a mor (raw humus) type, where the needles decay very slowly and the humus layer, produced from needles, moss, dead roots and fungal mycelia, is acid and lacks earthworms. This is a general feature of soils under conifers unless they are lime-rich or fertile loams. The characteristic dwarf shrub of spruce woods is the bilberry, which, in Fennoscandia, is nearly always accompanied by cowberry, wavy hair-grass and the mosses *Hylocomium splendens* and *Pleurozium schreberi*. Also frequent are hairy wood-rush *(Luzula pilosa)*, May lily *(Maianthemum bifolium)*, goldenrod *(Solidago virgaurea)*, twinflower *(Linnaea borealis)*, chickweed winter-green *(Trientalis europaea)*, various species of clubmoss *(Lycopodium)*, and true mosses such as the handsome *Ptilium crista-castrensis* and large species of *Dicranum*. Characteristic of somewhat richer woods are the oak fern *(Gymnocarpium dryopteris)* and such tall herbs as wood cranes-bill *(Geranium sylvaticum)*. On very fertile soils, mainly at higher altitudes, the blue sow-thistle *(Cicerbita alpina)* and the tall, handsome northern monk's-hood *Aconitum septentrionale* can be

Ivy *(Hedera helix)* is more often found in deciduous than coniferous woods, but is a common plant in spruce woods on the German hills. The flower-bearing branches have oval leaves instead of the familiar ivy-leaves and lack the usual small, clinging roots. The flowers open very late in the year and are pollinated by flies and wasps. Flowering period: September-November.

The bilberry *(Vaccinium myrtillus)* is very similar to the cowberry but can be distinguished by its deciduous leaves, which turn pinkish in late summer, and by its bright green, angled stem. It grows in almost any type of wood on acid soil as well as in heaths and mountain grasslands. Flowering period: April-June.

Chimaphila umbellata is a small shrub with leathery leaves whose flowers show its relationship to the wintergreens *(Pyrola* species). It is found in the more nutrient-rich pine woods, particularly in Fennoscandia. Flowering period: June-August.

Lily-of-the-valley *(Convallaria majalis)* is a widespread plant of dry woods, usually growing in calcareous soil. In the autumn, the white flowers are replaced by bright red berries. Flowering period: May-June.

found. In the southern and central parts of Fennoscandia the ground flora of spruce woods includes wood sorrel *(Oxalis acetosella)*, common violet *(Viola riviniana)*, wood anemone *(Anemone nemorosa)* and species of wintergreen *(Pyrola)* and related genera. The wetter woods have wood horsetail *(Equisetum sylvaticum)*, the reed-like grasses *Calamagrostis canescens* and *C. purpurea*, and several sedges and ferns. Where spruce woods occur on richer soils or on limestone, the ground flora may be reminiscent of deciduous woodlands, with sanicle *(Sanicula europaea)*, *Hepatica nobilis*, the pea *Lathyrus vernus*, and locally even ramsons *(Allium ursinum)* and dog's mercury *(Mercurialis perennis)*.

The native spruce woods on the German hills have a similar mixture of species, including bilberry, May lily and wood sorrel, but also the grass *Calamagrostis villosa*, ivy *(Hedera helix)*, hard fern *(Blechnum spicant)*, herbs like *Prenanthes purpurea*, and abundant suboceanic mosses such as *Rhytidiadelphus loreus* and *Plagiothecium undulatum*. When silver fir is present, it occurs in the lower range of the spruce and extends down into the beech forest. However, it does not compete very successfully with spruce and has decreased considerably during this century as forestry practice has allowed the spruce to extend downwards far into the beech zone, and to occupy new areas, such as the Vosges.

Spruce seedlings do not grow up readily in heavy shade and in nature effective regeneration is dependent on gaps in the canopy. These occur when trees, sometimes healthy, sometimes weakened by insect attack or fungal disease (to which spruce is more susceptible than pine) are blown down. Spruce is not as long-lived as pine—which may live for several centuries and, in the northern mountains, for almost a thousand years—and it is much less fire resistant. In the northernmost parts of its range and in the mountains, it seldom produces viable seeds. Instead, it reproduces by layering: the lowest branches, pressed down by the weight of snow and overgrown with moss, develop adventitious roots; their tips start to grow upwards and eventually they become partly or fully independent of the parent tree. These new trees are often badly deformed by desiccating winds and further damaged by very low night temperatures in late winter, when their resistance to frost has been weakened by periods of warm sunshine. A common feature of many northern conifers, especially spruce, is for trees at high altitudes and latitudes to have a very narrow crown. It has been suggested that this minimizes damage caused by the weight of snow or rime.

Subalpine birch forests

In Fennoscandia spruce ascends as high as or, in places, higher than pine except in the extreme northern parts of Norway and Finland. Both conifers eventually give way to a belt of birch *(Betula pubescens)* which continues to the tree-line. The birches are usually tall shrubs rather than trees, with several stems sprouting from the same base. The extent to which this birch zone is developed varies considerably but birch is not usually found in sites with a very deep snow cover.

Being deciduous and with a light canopy, these woods have a well-developed ground vegetation which differs from that of the pine and spruce woods only in having more alpine plants. Because of the cool climate and the absence of earthworms at this altitude the soil is hardly less acid and no better structured than it is under pine and spruce. Dwarf shrubs such as bilberry are again prominent, with much mountain crowberry *(Empetrum nigrum* subsp. *hermaphroditum)* on knolls and ridges where there is little snow cover. Lichen-rich birch woods are especially characteristic of the far north. Where the soils are flushed by seepage water and consequently more fertile, there are many tall and attractive herbs, for example, wood cranes-bill, globeflower *(Trollius europaeus)*, *Aconitum septentrionale*, alpine sow-thistle and melancholy thistle *(Cirsium helenioides)*. Frequently growing mixed with the birch are rowan *(Sorbus aucuparia)*, juniper and, especially along the banks of streams, various willows such as *Salix glauca, S. phylicifolia, S. lanata* and *S. lapponum*.

There are similar woods in Scotland, where they largely replace pine woods in the more oceanic western and north-western Highlands. They differ, however, in having the following southern or western species: hazel *(Corylus avellana)*, bluebell *(Hyacinthoides non-scripta)*, honeysuckle *(Lonicera periclymenum)* and great wood-rush *(Luzula sylvatica)*. In Iceland, birch woods once covered much of the island but they have been practically eliminated by grazing, chiefly by sheep.

The presence of birch at the limit of tree growth throughout the northern part of the region is thought to be due to the relatively oceanic climate, since east of the Kola

Rubus arcticus is a low-growing bramble, restricted to scrub and open woodland in Fennoscandia. Its dark red autumn berries are delicious to eat and form the basis of a much esteemed liqueur. Flowering period: June-August.

Right: On the most fertile sites, subalpine woods of birch *(Betula pubescens)* have a very rich flora of tall herbs. Growing here are round yellow globeflowers *(Trollius europaeus)*, mauve wood cranesbill *(Geranium sylvaticum)*, meadow buttercups *(Ranunculus acris)* in the foreground and, further back, large tufts of the fern *Matteucia struthiopteris*. Flowering period: June-August.

Subalpine birch woods are characteristically open so there is plenty of room between the trees for light to penetrate to the ground vegetation, which is often luxuriant.

Right: The monkshood *Aconitum septentrionale* (1) and alpine sow-thistle *(Cicerbita alpina)* (2) grow in northern communities of tall herbs on moist rich soils. Flowering period: monkshood, July-August, alpine sow-thistle July-September.

Below: The white 'petals' of the dwarf cornel *(Cornus suecica)* are modified leaves; the blackish purple centre consists of individual flowers. Flowering period: July-August.

When timber has been removed, branches and debris remain. This used to be burned to enrich the soil for seedling establishment.

1

2

Peninsula its place is taken by spruce and also larch *(Larix* species), which is not native in Fennoscandia. Elsewhere, birch is essentially a pioneer tree, eventually giving way to pine or spruce; in these subalpine woods, however, it forms the climax. Although in some places it regenerates by seed, more usually it grows from basal shoots. This results in groups of trees which may be extremely long lived, in spite of the relatively short life-span of the individual stems.

Fire and its effects

Forest fires were a feature of the coniferous forests of northern Fennoscandia long before man became an important factor but even pre-historic man increased their frequency. It has been demonstrated from studies of fire scars in the wood of both living and dead pines that dry pine woods in southern Swedish Lappland used to suffer from spontaneous fires about twice a century. The results of fire are not always devastating. Some pine trees survive and following burning the soil is better suited for the establishment of seedlings of both pine and birch. Spruce forests, which occur on somewhat moister sites, burn readily but less frequently and are always killed except where the ground is too wet for the fire to take hold. The result is that pine has spread at the expense of spruce and now occupies sites which would appear to be favourable to spruce. The subalpine birch woods never burn spontaneously.

The effects of pre-industrial man

As already mentioned, the widespread destruction of the native forest cover in north-west Europe began in the Neolithic period, around 3000BC, and has continued at an ever-increasing pace up to this century. In the Neolithic and Bronze Ages, human activity in Fennoscandia was most pronounced in Denmark and the coastal areas of southern Sweden and Norway. The method usually used by these primitive farmers, burnbeating or *swidden* farming, was similar to the shifting cultivation which is still used in tropical countries. Every year large areas of forest were felled, burned and sown, first with barley or wheat and later, from the Roman Iron Age onwards, mostly with rye. They were then left to be invaded by grasses and herbs, which were first used for hay and then for grazing. Gradually the trees regenerated and eventually the area was burnbeaten again.

Forest fires were often started deliberately to improve the grazing. Large areas of forest were transformed into semi-permanent hay-meadows with scattered trees or into wooded, fenced pastures. More widespread still was the practice of allowing cattle, goats, sheep and horses to graze the unfenced forests. During the summer animals were often taken to graze around simple summer dwellings and byres, often at a considerable distance from the lowland farms. This seasonal movement of livestock is known as transhumance. Burning and grazing caused the ground flora to change as well as promoting the regeneration of certain forest trees, such as birch, while discouraging others. The subsequent development of heathlands in the western parts of our region is dealt with in Chapter 5.

Forest timber was, of course, used for firewood and for building. In years of famine the inner bark of the pine was collected, dried, ground and mixed with flour. Pinewood, especially stumps but also trunks killed by strip-barking, was used as a source of wood-tar, an important export item in the days of sailing ships. The collection of resin was less widely practised and probably ceased long ago in north-west Europe. With the development of local smelting industries, enormous quantities of wood were required for charcoal.

Modern forestry

Modern forestry is almost exclusively concerned with conifers rather than deciduous trees. There are several reasons for this, one being that the long fibres of conifer wood are superior for paper-making. Another is simply that conifers usually grow faster and reach commercial size more quickly, so producing a higher volume of timber for a given area. With the replacement of oakwood by iron for ship-building, coniferous softwood was perfectly adequate for most purposes—planks for the construction industry, pit-props for mines, pulp for paper and, more recently, for the manufacture of such secondary products as chip-board. The tendency to grow more and more conifers has scarcely been affected by the higher state subsidy for planting hardwood which is available, for example, in Great Britain. Another major factor is that much of the afforestation is on poor quality marginal land which is unsuitable for commercial crops of deciduous trees.

Widespread afforestation (which in Great Britain really dates from the first world war and reverses two thousand years of deforestation) and the increasing pace at which modern forestry practices are being applied to existing forests, have together brought about dramatic changes in the landscape of north-west Europe. In many newly afforested areas as well as in a large number of the older woodlands, exotic species or improved or selected strains of native species have been introduced. The most important newcomers in the west of our region are the Sitka spruce (Picea sitchensis), western hemlock (Tsuga heterophylla), Douglas fir (Pseudotsuga menziesii) and lodgepole pine (Pinus contorta), all from western and north-west North America, the Japanese larch (Larix kaempferi), and the Corsican pine

(Pinus nigra) from southern Europe. However, in Fennoscandia and Germany most coniferous forests are still planted with native Scots pine and Norway spruce, although lodgepole pine is increasingly used.

Around the turn of the century, selective felling of larger trees was widely practised in the native northern forests. This had very little effect on the ground flora but it resulted in permanent patchiness from poor regeneration, probably because the saplings growing in the gaps produced by felling had to compete with the increased root-growth of the remaining trees. Furthermore, because these remaining trees were either too weak or malformed, they largely failed to respond to selective felling, which therefore became less attractive commercially than clear felling. With the diversification of industry and the development of pulp factories, trees of all sizes could be used and clear felling became standard practice. The areas felled were at first not unduly large, sometimes no more than small glades which could easily be seeded naturally from the surrounding trees. Alternatively, a few of the original pines were left to provide seed. (Spruce trees cannot be left in this way to supply seeds as they are likely to blow down when suddenly exposed.)

Although other areas have increased their output, Fennoscandia is still one of the world's main timber-producing regions. Partly because of the slow rate of growth in its harsh climate (conifers take over a hundred years to reach marketable size in northern Fennoscandia), the line between economic success and failure for the forestry industry is a fine one. International competition as well as high labour, transport and other costs have made it essential to mechanize and reduce costs to a minimum. Large areas are therefore clear felled; in fact at any one time between 7 and 10 per cent of the forest area must be in a clear-felled state if it is to produce the maximum sustained yield.

There are many problems in modern forestry. Too much coarse brushwood left after felling or thinning may lead to an increase in pests, for example the spruce bark beetle. Yet the practice of burning brushwood after felling has now been largely abandoned. Regeneration from selected seed pines or from the surrounding forest is increasingly being replaced by planting, with scarification of the humus layer, and even ploughing being used to encourage seedling growth. However, many seedlings may be destroyed by pine weevils (Hylobius abietis). Large populations of the larvae develop in the old stumps and the adult weevils eat the thin bark of the young seedlings. The young conifers which survive soon find themselves in competition with broad-leaved saplings or coppice shoots sprouting from the stumps of felled trees, especially birch. The shoots can be controlled by spraying herbicides from the air but this also affects the ground flora, including the important berry-bearing dwarf shrubs. Aerial

spraying is very unpopular and is at present prohibited in Fennoscandia, but not in the British Isles. Another less obvious result of clear felling is the raising of the water-table, which may lead to waterlogging of the young trees.

Densely planted seedlings eventually produce an impenetrable forest, with the young trees weakened by excessive competition and their shade so dense that there is virtually no ground flora, especially under spruce. It is a curious fact that there is far less self-pruning (the falling off of dead branches) in coniferous plantations than in naturally regenerating woods, so the close canopy becomes impenetrable. Such conditions can be improved by reducing planting density, pruning or thinning the saplings.

Conifer plantations are now prominent and familiar features even in much of the western part of our region where native coniferous forests were originally lacking, as for example over most of the British Isles and in western Jutland. They have been planted on land which was once covered with deciduous woodland, open heath or moorland, mires, or poor pasture. Present-day forestry affects the landscape profoundly both as regards ecology and scenery.

One effect of replacing broad-leaved woodland by conifers is to bring about a deterioration of the topsoil, the crumb structure and mull humus of the better soils under hardwoods changing to an impoverished raw humus soil. There is some evidence that a similar deterioration occurred naturally long ago in native northern coniferous forests, a change which encouraged the less demanding dwarf shrubs at the expense of the herbaceous plants.

The increasing acidity of rain, caused by widespread and often long-distance pollution, chiefly of sulphur dioxide, is a potential threat to forestry over large areas, including the southern half of Fennoscandia, but so far definite evidence of damage has been found only near certain cities and factories. Another, less obvious long-term threat is from heavy metal pollution.

There are two very different attitudes to the effects of present-day forestry on scenery and amenities. The British public, for example, likes an open landscape and resents anything which restricts the view. In Germany there is genuine affection for the free-growing *Wald*, as opposed to the impenetrability and gloom of the *Forst* (plantation). In Fennoscandia the forests play an integral part in the traditions and culture of the peoples. There the collecting of berries or mushrooms, bird-watching and shooting of game (especially the very valuable moose), as well as sports such as orienteering and cross-country skiing are favourite open-air activities in the native forests. According to *allemansrätt* (everyman's right), such activities, with the exception of shooting, are regarded as a universal right in Fennoscandia, a right which is actually being seriously threatened by many aspects of present-day, large-scale forestry management.

4
Natural and agricultural grasslands

Our Palaeolithic ancestors hunted over the treeless plains of southern Europe while Scandinavia and much of Britain and the north German plain still lay under ice during the last glaciation. As already mentioned, when the climate grew warmer and the ice-sheets receded, forest spread northwards to cover the former hunting grounds. Europe became a forested continent, and for thousands of years grassland must have been reduced to no more than scattered fragments. Throughout this period, man seems to have had only a rather modest influence on the landscape. With the beginning of Neolithic agriculture, grassland began to expand again. From then onwards, progressive opening up of the forest and the spread of grassland and arable cultivation followed the development of settled farming.

Fertile agricultural grasslands

For many centuries, permanent grasslands have played an important role in the pattern of farming in north-west Europe, either as pastures grazed by livestock, or as meadows mown for hay to provide the stock with winter keep. The grasslands close to farms and villages generally occupied deep fertile soils which had formerly borne lowland forest of oak, beech or other broad-leaved trees. They were often carefully managed to maintain their fertility and traditional farming practices often increased the mineral nutrients of the farmland at the expense of rough pasture and forest.

Fertile agricultural grasslands of this kind dominated much of the farming landscape of north-west Europe until very recent times. Fragments of similar grasslands are to be found around tracks and habitations even in areas with little cultivation and they are among the most widespread types of vegetation in our region. The sown leys of modern intensive farming are agriculturally very productive but in terms of numbers of species they are a poor substitute for these traditional grasslands.

Ox-eye daisies (*Leucanthemum vulgare*) are a characteristic component of unimproved pastures. Here they are growing with red clover (*Trifolium pratense*), yellow rattle (*Rhinanthus minor*), ribwort plantain (*Plantago lanceolata*) and the grasses *Anthoxanthum odoratum*, *Cynosurus cristatus*, *Dactylis glomerata* and *Poa pratensis*. Flowering period: June-August.

Roadside verges are often the only places where grassland similar to that of unimproved hay meadows can still be found. Amongst the tall grasses, cow parsley (*Anthriscus sylvestris*) makes a splendid sight, while roadside trees such as hawthorn (*Crataegus monogyna*) are covered in blossom. Later in the season, other tall herbs such as hogweed (*Heracleum sphondylium*) and meadow cranesbill (*Geranium pratense*) are interspersed among flowering grasses. Flowering period: April–June.

Hay-making on agriculturally improved grassland below a steeper slope with semi-natural grassland. Beyond is a typical view of rough-grazing on chalk with a scattering of shrubs. In the foreground is the musk thistle (*Carduus nutans*), with its characteristically drooping heads. Flowering period: May–August.

Most of the turf is made up of a few common grasses: rye-grass (*Lolium perenne*), red fescue (*Festuca rubra*), crested dog's-tail (*Cynosurus cristatus*), the meadow-grasses (*Poa pratensis* and *P. trivialis*), timothy (*Phleum pratense*), cock's foot (*Dactylis glomerata*), *Bromus hordeaceus* and Yorkshire-fog (*Holcus lanatus*) are all but universal, and are joined on acid soils by sweet vernal-grass (*Anthoxanthum odoratum*) and common bent (*Agrostis cappilaris*). Broad-leaved herbs such as yarrow (*Achillea millefolium*), daisy (*Bellis perennis*), common mouse-ear (*Cerastium (fontanum*), the creeping thistle (*Cirsium arvense*), the plantains *Plantago lanceolata* and *P. major*, meadow buttercup (*Ranunculus acris*), common sorrel (*Rumex acetosa*), dandelion (*Taraxacum officinale*), lesser trefoil (*Trifolium dubium*) and white clover (*T. repens*) are common. Despite the fact that all these plants are grazed, they are able to continue growing because the growing points and buds are usually at soil level and so escape damage. Some heavily grazed pastures may contain few species beyond this list.

Meadows which are cut for hay are different in character from pastures which are regularly grazed, but there is no sharp distinction between the two. A piece of grassland may be left for hay only at intervals, and it was common to put stock to graze on the 'aftermath' when a meadow had been mown. But in grasslands which are kept primarily for hay, many grasses and larger dicotyledonous herbs which are suppressed or eliminated by grazing, become prominent; these species disappear or play only a minor role in permanent pastures. Thus grasses such as meadow foxtail (*Alopecurus pratensis*) and false oat-grass (*Arrhenatherum elatius*), broad-leaved herbs such as hogweed (*Heracleum sphondylium*) field scabious (*Knautia arvensis*), common knapweed (*Centaurea nigra*), cow-parsley (*Anthriscus sylvestris*) and meadow crane's-bill (*Geranium pratense*) are characteristic of hay-meadows and of roadside communities which, like meadows, are not constantly grazed. False oat-grass is particularly characteristic of ungrazed grasslands on base-rich soils in the more oceanic and southern parts of the region, accompanied by such species as oxeye daisy

Yarrow *(Achillea millefolium)* is a plant commonly found in many neutral grasslands and waste places. The flowering heads are complex, with each 'flower' made up of many individual florets, as in a daisy. The leaf is very distinctive, being divided into hundreds of tiny segments. Flowering period: June-August.

Common knapweed *(Centaurea nigra)* is a common plant of hay meadows, grasslands and roadside verges. Apart from their attractive red-purple florets, the heads have an interesting ring of bracts, each with a triangular, comb-like appendage at the tip. Flowering period: June-September.

Daisies *(Bellis perennis)* are abundant in short grassland, particularly where it is grazed or regularly mown. The way the plant grows with its rosette of leaves, often pressed closely to the ground, and its stem apex at soil level means that the daisy benefits when grazing or mowing removes taller plants. Flowering period: March-October.

(Leucanthemum vulgare), meadow vetchling *(Lathyrus pratensis)*, wild parsnip *(Pastinaca sativa)*, tufted vetch *(Vicia cracca)* and bush vetch *(V. sepium)*.

In the south-eastern parts of the region, yellow oat-grass *(Trisetum flavescens)* plays an important part in montane meadows, with, for instance, lady's-mantle *(Alchemilla* species), northern hawk's-beard *(Crepis mollis)*, wood crane's-bill *(Geranium sylvaticum)*, the rampion *Phyteuma orbiculare* and red campion *(Silene dioica)*. Similar herb-rich meadows occur in Scandinavia and upland areas of northern Britain where they traditionally played an important role in providing hay as winter keep for livestock. Although these meadows lack some of the Continental species, lady's-mantle, wood crane's-bill, water avens *(Geum rivale)* and

great burnet *(Sanguisorba officinalis)* are often abundant, with, in damper places, melancholy thistle *(Cirsium helenioides)*, marsh hawk's-beard *(Crepis paludosa)* and globeflower *(Trollius europaeus)*. Sedges are abundant, notably *Carex panicea*, along with grasses such as common bent, sweet vernal-grass, quaking-grass *(Briza media)*, the hair-grasses *Deschampsia caespitosa* and *D. flexuosa*, sheep's-fescue *(Festuca ovina)*, red fescue, purple moor-grass *(Molinia caerulea)*, mountain melick *(Melica nutans)* and mat-grass *(Nardus stricta)*, the detailed composition of the turf varying from place to place. In the mainly forested landscape of Sweden, a scattering of broad-leaved trees such as birch *(Betula* species), grey alder *(Alnus incana)* or rowan *(Sorbus aucuparia)* was often left, giving characteristic 'park

Besides having many grasses, northern and montane hay meadows are typically rich in flowers. This meadow has meadow buttercup *(Ranunculus acris)*, red clover *(Trifolium pratense)*, ribwort plantain *(Plantago lanceolata)*, daisy *(Bellis perennis)* and yellow-rattle *(Rhinanthus minor)*, which is partly parasitic on other plants, often grasses. Flowering period: June-August.

Water avens *(Geum rivale)* is usually a plant of river banks or fens, but it can be easily found in the damper northern and montane hay meadows. Its flowers are usually nodding and perhaps not very conspicuous. Like its more noticeable relative, the bright yellow-flowered wood avens *(Geum urbanum)*, it makes use of animals for seed dispersal, having styles with a hook at the end Flowering period: May-September.

Right: Meadow buttercups *(Ranunculus acris)* can be very abundant in upland meadows, but although they are very pretty to look at, they do not add much to the quality of the pasture. Meadows of this type are increasingly being ploughed and reseeded with high quality grass mixtures. Flowering period: May-July.

The yellow thistle *Cirsium oleraceum* is typical of wet meadows in mainland Europe. It is easily distinguished by its pale yellow heads, surrounded by the yellowish uppermost leaves. Flowering period: July-September.

Right: Marsh marigold *(Caltha palustris)* is widespread throughout our region where it occurs in marshes, fens, ditches and wet woods wherever there is a moderate supply of nutrients. The plant becomes most luxuriant in partial shade. Flowering period: March-July.

Often growing with water avens in the wetter meadows is ragged-robin *(Lychnis flos-cuculi)*. Here it is the only obvious flower in the meadow. Its ragged appearance is caused by each of its five petals being deeply divided into four. Flowering period: May-June.

meadows'. Under modern conditions, the traditional labour-intensive management of such meadows is no longer economic and they have largely become used as rough pasture, or been allowed to revert to forest. The corresponding grasslands in Iceland are generally less luxuriant and poorer in species, but a number of northern plants occur quite commonly, such as the grass *Festuca vivipara*, the bedstraw *Galium boreale* and the knotgrass *Polygonum viviparum*.

Wet sites bring in a new range of species. Wild angelica *(Angelica sylvestris)*, marsh-marigold *(Caltha palustris)*, various sedges *(Carex* species), marsh-orchids *(Dactylorhiza* species), meadowsweet *(Filipendula ulmaria)*, yellow flag *(Iris pseudacorus)*, rushes *(Juncus* species) and ragged-robin *(Lychnis flos-cuculi)* are common in wet meadows; and the striking yellowish thistle *Cirsium oleraceum* is characteristic of this type of situation over much of mainland Europe. In some places valley-floor meadows have been extensively irrigated with systems of weirs and ditches. Water meadows of this kind were common in southern England in the eighteenth and nineteenth centuries. Winter flooding brought in quantities of silt which acted as a fertilizer. Such meadows were valued for the 'early bite' they provided for sheep in March and April as well as for the heavy crops of hay they could yield later in the season. However, they needed

51

The foxglove *(Digitalis purpurea)* is pollinated by bumble bees *(Bombus* species) which crawl right into the flower to obtain pollen and nectar. The deep purple spots on a white ground are supposed to help pollination by guiding the bumble bees to the food source. Flowering period: June-September.

much labour for upkeep and generally little now remains in these low-lying fields but the indistinct pattern of the silted-up ditches. The fritillary *(Fritillaria meleagris)* is particularly characteristic of such meadows.

In the humid climate of oceanic western Europe, wet agricultural grasslands occur widely on acid soils, for example on shales and clayey glacial drift in western Britain and Ireland. These grasslands have relatively few species. The rushes *Juncus effusus* and *J. acutiflorus* are generally prominent, along with marsh ragwort *(Senecio aquaticus)*, the St John's-wort *Hypericum tetrapterum*, common fleabane *(Pulicaria dysenterica)* and hemp agrimony *(Eupatorium cannabinum)*. These rushy meadows and pastures merge into purple moor-grass communities which ecologically and in species composition, occupy an intermediate position between grasslands and the mire communities described in Chapter 8. They have a very variable but rather characteristic flora including such species as sneezewort *(Achillea ptarmica)*, meadow thistle *(Cirsium dissectum)*, devil's-bit scabious *(Succisa pratensis)*, marsh valerian *(Valeriana dioica)* and, in mainland Europe, marsh gentian *(Gentiana pneumonanthe)*. The hay-meadows described earlier are normally mown green, sometimes several times in a season. Fen meadows of the unpalatable purple moor-grass on lowland peat used to be cut in late

Left: Fritillaries *(Fritillaria meleagris)* have been greatly affected by changes in agricultural practice. Formerly fairly common in wet meadows and pastures, particularly water-meadows, they are becoming rarer as these are drained. Flowering period: April-May.

The bright yellow flowers of the common rockrose *(Helianthemum nummularium)* are a familiar sight on drier grasslands of chalk and limestone. Flowering period: June-September.

Cowslips *(Primula veris)* are most commonly found on calcareous soils in pastures or short grassland. They are becoming less common as grasslands are ploughed and reseeded, but have colonized such habitats as railway embankments and motorway verges. Flowering period: April-May.

summer to provide litter for livestock. This practice was once widespread in the Netherlands, Germany and the fenlands of East Anglia.

Semi-natural grasslands

Apart from the fertile grasslands which obviously form a part of the agricultural scene, substantial tracts of more natural grasslands still remain in northern and western Europe. These were traditionally used as rough pasture, and the practice still continues in many places. Most would quickly revert to scrub and then to forest if it were not for grazing by sheep, cattle or rabbits. They have generally not been manured, and apart from grazing (or, in a few cases, burning) have undergone little deliberate management.

GRASSLANDS ON CHALK AND LIMESTONE

Among the most widespread and attractive semi-natural grasslands are those on chalk, limestone and other base-rich rocks. They occupy soils which are typically rich in calcium and often in organic matter, but poor in available nitrogen and phosphate. Although they are freely drained and often give the impression of being very dry in summer, the chalk and other softer limestones are porous and hold considerable reserves of water which the deep root systems of the plants

Orchids such as these pyramidal orchids *(Anacamptis pyramidalis)* are particularly characteristic of grasslands over chalk and limestone. These derive their name from the conical form of the younger dense-flowered spike. Flowering period: June-August.

are able to exploit. Drought is therefore less of a hazard here than it is in many habitats that appear at first sight to be more favourable. Harder limestones provide similar conditions, provided the soil is reasonably deep and the climate not too dry. The grasses form a close turf, sometimes only a few centimetres high, but this depends on slope, aspect and grazing. Calcareous grasslands are often strikingly rich in species since most of the taller and faster-growing plants of the fertile agricultural grasslands are absent, enabling smaller, slower-growing species to survive. Thirty or more species of flowering plants can often be found within a square metre.

The commonest dominant grasses are the brome *Bromus erectus*, sheep's-fescue, red fescue and tor-grass *(Brachypodium pinnatum)*. Blue moor-grass *(Sesleria albicans)* is more local but dominates considerable tracts of grassland on thin soils over calcareous rocks in Ireland, northern England, the hilly areas of central and southern Germany and, very locally, in northern France. The grasses are accompanied by a very characteristic flora including the grasses *Briza media*, *Helictotrichon pratense* and *Koeleria macrantha*, the sedges *Carex caryophyllea* and *C. flacca*, and such calcicole broad-leaved herbs as kidney vetch *(Anthyllis vulneraria)*, squinancywort *(Asperula cynanchica)*, dwarf thistle *(Cirsium acaule)*, common rock-rose *(Helianthemum nummularium)*, burnet-saxifrage *(Pimpinella saxifraga)*, salad burnet *(Sanguisorba minor)*, small scabious *(Scabiosa columbaria)* and pasque flower *(Pulsatilla vulgaris)*, as well as pyramidal orchid *(Anacamptis pyramidalis)* and various other orchids. Some of these chalk and limestone communities, especially those on the thin soils of steep slopes, may have existed continuously as grassland ever since Neolithic farmers began clearing the forest. Often, however, they show signs of former cultivation or disturbance in Iron Age, mediaeval or more recent times. The defensive earthworks thrown up by the La Tène Celts around their hill forts on chalk and limestone in the first century BC often now bear fine, species-rich calcareous grasslands.

In contrast, chalk and limestone grasslands of recent origin are typically poor in species. They often include the widespread, fast-growing species of the fertile agricultural grasslands, possibly because these areas have been re-seeded by man, or because they are slightly more fertile, or merely because these common species can colonize an area much more rapidly than the rarer or more local calcicole species.

Recognizably similar limestone grassland communities, bright with flowers in early summer, occur throughout our region. These communities vary greatly in detail. South of the English Channel, species such as spiny field eryngo *(Eryngium campestre)* and cypress spurge *(Euphorbia cyparissias)* are a conspicuous feature of calcareous districts

The pasque flower *(Pulsatilla vulgaris)* is one of the most beautiful species of dry calcareous grasslands, perhaps because of the combination of its purple petals with their silky white hairs and its bright yellow stamens. The fruits are topped by a long silky plume. Flowering period: April-May.

Goldilocks *(Aster linosyris)* is strongly continental, being characteristic of the steppe grasslands of eastern Europe. In our region, it is restricted to relatively few hot, dry limestone sites from the islands of Gotland and Öland to western Britain. Flowering period: August-September.

Wall germander *(Teucrium chamaedrys),* another plant of southern Europe, is found on the hottest, driest limestone grasslands in the south of the region, reaching as far north as the hard chalk cliffs of the lower Seine valley. Flowering period: May-September.

Left: the horseshoe vetch *(Hippocrepis comosa)* is a species from the south of the region which reaches as far north as the Rhine, Belgium and southern Scotland. It gets its name from its pod, which breaks up into 3 to 6 horseshoe-shaped segments. Flowering period: May-July.

The feather grass *Stipa pennata* is more typical of the steppes of south and central Europe, but it does reach the drier grasslands of France and Germany. A closely related species, *S. joannis,* reaches southern Sweden.

but in southern Britain they are local and rare. Farther north, dwarf thistle and horseshoe vetch *(Hippocrepis comosa)* become rarer and more restricted in habitat until at their northern limit in England they are closely confined to warm, south- or west-facing slopes on shallow limestone soils. Further north still, and at higher altitudes, the southern and lowland species are scarce or absent, and northern and montane species, often sensitive to drought, begin to appear even in quite freely-drained grasslands. Examples are common butterwort *(Pinguicula vulgaris),* bird's-eye primrose *(Primula farinosa)* and the clubmoss *Selaginella selaginoides.*

DRY CALCAREOUS GRASSLANDS

In the hotter, drier areas, especially on hard limestones, the character of the grassland may be strikingly different. The grass cover is open, many of the common species of the widespread calcareous grasslands are missing, and their place is taken by a group of plants of notably southern distribution. Summer drought is clearly an important factor in this habitat. Grasslands of this type occur widely in the mountains of southern France, merging southwards into the Mediterranean *garrigue.* They extend northwards into our region as increasingly scattered fragments on particularly warm, dry southern slopes. It is no coincidence that many

grasslands of this kind are in well known wine-growing or tourist regions. Thus white rock-rose *(Helianthemum apenninum)*, the restharrow *Ononis natrix*, the spurge *Euphorbia seguieri*, wall germander *(Teucrium chamaedrys)*, goldilocks *(Aster linosyris)* and the grass *Melica ciliata* grow together on the hard chalk slopes of the Seine cliffs from Mantes to Les Andelys in northern France. White rock-rose and goldilocks reappear north of the English Channel at Torbay together with honewort *(Trinia glauca)*, and again near Weston-super-Mare in Somerset with honewort, the sedge *Carex humilis* and the grass *Koeleria vallesiana*. White rock-rose reaches its north-eastern limit in fragments of comparable grasslands in central Germany: near Würzburg it grows with honewort, goldilocks and *Carex humilis*; in the Unstrut valley south-west of Leipzig it is found in dry grasslands which include the sage *Teucrium montanum* and *Carex humilis*.

Several of the species that have been mentioned, for example goldilocks and *Carex humilis*, are strongly continental in their distributions, reaching into the steppe grasslands of eastern Europe. Together with field wormwood *(Artemisia campestris)*, the grasses *Phleum phleoides* and *Stipa* species, spiked speedwell *(Veronica spicata)* and many other plants they represent a 'steppe' element which can be traced in many of the drier and more open grasslands on base-rich soils in central and north-west Europe. These species are well represented in Sweden, particularly on the Baltic islands of Gotland and Öland, especially the latter where Linnaeus described '. . . red limestone covered by soil to a finger's thickness or by no soil at all.' The characteristic and beautiful feather grass *Stipa joannis* does not grow on these islands, but reaches its very isolated north-western limit on dry calcareous soils in Västergötland, between lakes Vänern and Vättern in southern Sweden. Farther south, 'steppe' species grow in dry limestone grasslands at many scattered sites in the sunny valleys of central and southern Germany as, for instance, in the Rhineland west of Mainz and, just outside the region, on the Kaiserstühl at the western edge of the Black Forest. A few, such as Spanish catch-fly *(Silene otites)*, field wormwood and the grass *Phleum phleoides*, reach the grass-heaths of East Anglia. Paradoxically, in the British Isles several markedly continental species, such as goldilocks, hoary rock-rose *(Helianthemum canum)* and spiked speedwell, occur chiefly close to the west coast, where the hard Carboniferous limestone cliffs provide appropriate soil conditions which eastern England cannot match. Probably these cliffs also offered an open habitat for grassland species during the period when the Post-glacial forest reached its greatest extent. The present distribution of these continental species brings them into close juxtaposition with both

The sheep's sorrel *(Rumex acetosella)* is a short-lived perennial that grows in the poorest sandy soils. It grows often to only a few centimetres in height and where common gives a red tint to the vegetation. Flowering period: May-August.

On very dry, acid, sandy soils grasses grow sparsely. Here the greyish grass *Corynephorus canescens* grows with reddish sheep's sorrel (*Rumex acetosella*) and the white flowers of the mignonette *Sesamoides canescens*. Gaps between the plants may be bare or covered by the moss *Rhacomitrium canescens*. Flowering period: May-July.

The wild strawberry (*Fragaria vesca*) is common in woods, scrub or grassland on richer soil It can sometimes dominate areas in woods on calcareous soils. The fruit is very much smaller than that of the cultivated strawberry which is a hybrid between a species from eastern North America and one from Chile. Flowering period: April-July.

oceanic and calcifuge plants, which grow where the humid oceanic climate causes local leaching and acidification of the surface layers of the limestone soil. Striking instances of such disparate mixtures of species can be seen in the Gower peninsula of South Wales, and especially in the Burren district just south of Galway Bay in western Ireland.

Over long periods of time, accumulation of organic matter and the leaching effects of rain draining through the soil bring about changes, so that free calcium carbonate and certain other nutrients are removed and the surface layers of the soil become acidified. Conditions tend to become progressively less favourable for calcicoles or species with exacting nutrient requirements, and more favourable for calcifuge species of poor soils. The effects of leaching are often obvious on chalk and limestone soils, especially in the more oceanic parts of the region. The most characteristic calcareous grasslands are therefore found on steep slopes where erosion nullifies the effect of leaching. By contrast, the gentler slopes and flat summits have deeper, neutral or acid soils with a very different vegetation (see below). Limestone soils with surface leaching sometimes bear very striking and attractive 'limestone heaths' in which calcicole species grow intimately intermixed with gorse (*Ulex* species), heather (*Calluna vulgaris*) and bell heather (*Erica cinerea*).

DRY GRASSLANDS OF SANDY AND ACID SOILS

On sandy soils, such as the sandy glacial deposits of northern Germany, northern France and East Anglia, the grasslands are much thinner with bare gaps between the plants, which are themselves tolerant of the very dry infertile acid conditions. A characteristic grass is *Corynephorus canescens*, which plays an important role in stabilizing inland dunes. It forms a thin, dry turf, often in company with sheep's-fescue, brown bent (*Agrostis canina*) and sand sedge (*Carex arenaria*). Mosses and lichens, such as *Rhacomitrium canescens*, *Polytrichum piliferum* and *Cladonia*, are often abundant and conspicuous, forming a carpet dotted with small herbaceous plants such as shepherd's cress (*Teesdalia nudicaulis*), sheep's-bit (*Jasione montana*) and sheep's sorrel (*Rumex acetosella*). Similar communities in East Anglia lack *Corynephorus*. On more stable acid soils, these grasslands give way to *Calluna* heath (see Chapter 5). Where the glacial deposits are more chalky, the grasslands increasingly resemble calcareous grasslands, forming a complex of communities including most of the notably eastern and 'steppe' species of eastern England. The extent of these grass-heaths has tended to ebb and flow with the changing fortunes of agriculture, the grass-heaths spreading over abandoned, infertile, sandy arable fields during periods of agricultural depression, and being reduced again to patches as the land has been recultivated at times of high crop prices.

Comparable grasslands occur on the more stable areas of old coastal dunes (see Chapter 10) and fragmentary patches of grassland communities, rich in annuals and small herbs, are very widespread on thin, dry gravel soils or in pockets on rock outcrops. They typically include such annual grasses as *Aira praecox*, *A. caryophyllea* and *Vulpia bromoides*, annual herbs such as the clovers *Trifolium arvense* and *T. scabrum*, the mouse-ear *Cerastium semidecandrum*, the forget-me-not *Myosotis ramosissima*, often a thin cover of such perennial grasses as sheep's-fescue, common and brown bents, and varying quantities of the smaller succulent stonecrops (*Sedum* species). Communities of this kind, with abundant *Aira praecox* and English stonecrop (*Sedum anglicum*), are particularly prominent around acid rock outcrops on exposed coastal cliffs in western Britain, Ireland and north-west France.

LOWLAND HEATHY GRASSLANDS
AND ACID UPLAND PASTURES

Over much of western Europe, grazing of *Calluna* heath leads to the development of acid grasslands dominated by common bent, sheep's-fescue and mat-grass. In northern Germany and the Netherlands the dry heaths and the grasslands that replace them under heavy grazing are often rather rich in species with, for instance, heath dog-violet (*Viola canina*), common milkwort (*Polygala vulgaris*) and mouse-ear hawkweed (*Hieracium pilosella*). In the humid and oceanic climate of the British Isles these species tend to be more limited to sharply drained, exposed coastal sites, or to somewhat base-rich soils. Both in Britain and in mainland Europe, lowland grass-heaths have declined, as a result of agricultural improvement, to a fraction of their extent a century ago.

Typical of northern and western Britain, and often dominating the upland landscape, are the hill pastures, poor in species but covering thousands of hectares of acid soils. Occupying ground that under natural conditions would generally have supported acid oak wood, these pastures are both the product and the basis of traditional sheep farming in Wales, northern England and much of Scotland. On well-drained slopes the dominant grasses are common bent and sheep's-fescue. Among the few associated plants are sweet vernal-grass, heath bedstraw (*Galium saxatile*), tormentil (*Potentilla erecta*), field wood-rush (*Luzula campestris*), and mosses such as *Dicranum scoparium*, *Hypnum cupressiforme* var. *ericetorum* and *Pleurozium schreberi*, with variable amounts of heather and bilberry (*Vaccinium myrtillus*) on the more acid soils or where the grazing is less intense. On the better soils the turf is rather richer in species, with a scattering of plants such as harebell (*Campanula rotundifolia*), bird's-foot-trefoil (*Lotus corniculatus*), common milkwort and wild thyme (*Thymus praecox*). On less well-drained sites the last

The common milkwort (*Polygala vulgaris*) grows in short, usually grazed grasslands or heaths on all but the most acid soils. Its very variable flower colour can be blue, pink or white. On more acid soils it is replaced by *Polygala serpyllifolia* which, though very similar, has at least some of its lower leaves arranged in opposite pairs rather than all alternately. Flowering period: May-September.

A frequent colonist of less grazed chalk grassland is the dog rose (*Rosa canina*). Once established, its strongly hooked prickles deter large animals from feeding on it. Flowering period: June-July.

Bracken *(Pteridium aquilinum)* is one of the few really common and successful ferns. This is largely because it can spread widely by its long underground rhizome which most other ferns do not possess. Bracken is at its most beautiful in autumn, when its rich golden brown adds splendour to thc landscape.

group of plants is lacking and mat-grass becomes dominant, forming a harsh turf which is much poorer grazing; mat-grass dominance is also a characteristic result of overgrazing by sheep. Damp conditions bring in such plants as lousewort (Pedicularis sylvatica), the sedges *Carex binervis, C. panicea* and *C. nigra*, and the rushes *Juncus effusus* and *J. squarrosus*. The last species is often dominant together with mat-grass on the shallow peat of badly drained spurs and summits. In wet conditions on the gentle lower slopes or valley bottoms the *Agrostis-Festuca* and *Nardus* grasslands give way to communities dominated by *Molinia* and rushes, often containing the sedge *Carex echinata*, the marsh violet *(Viola palustris)*, and the erect moss *Polytrichum commune*. With their abundance of *Sphagnum* species and other plants of waterlogged habitats, they are transitional to the mires described in Chapter 8.

BRACKEN

Over most of its European range, the bracken fern *(Pteridium aquilinum)* is a plant of acid woodland. In Britain, Ireland and western France it also becomes an aggressive colonist of well-drained bent-fescue grasslands. Bracken in hill pastures is not wholly without virtue. In the past it was widely used as litter for livestock and for thatching; the dry fronds were used for fuel, and it was burned for potash. Bracken has been used as fodder, the fresh or dried fronds for cattle and horses, and the rhizomes mainly for pigs. It has even been included in the human diet. The young shoots, when cooked, are said to taste like asparagus, and the ground rhizomes have been used in many places to eke out flour in hard times. It is now known that if it is eaten in substantial quantity or over a period of time, bracken can cause several types of poisoning in livestock, and may lead to cancer in animals and humans; it is today generally regarded simply as a troublesome weed in pastures. A scattering of bracken fronds may have little influence on the composition or vigour of the pasture; indeed they may provide welcome shelter and a degree of protection from frost in winter. But a dense stand of mature bracken can shade out almost all other vegetation. At best only an impoverished turf will survive.

Bracken can become established from spores, and this must be important in the colonization of new areas. The spores germinate to produce a delicate prothallus which needs a moist habitat such as a rabbit burrow or a rocky hedgebank, and sometimes rings or semicircles of bracken can be seen around such spots. Once established, bracken spreads over shorter distances by vigorous growth of its underground rhizomes, so that it is difficult to control or eradicate. It can be kept in check by repeated cutting, crushing or trampling by stock, but any of these treatments must be applied regularly and persistently to be effective. Modern chemical herbicides give good results but are relatively expensive to apply and generally leave a good deal of living rhizome in the ground, so that treatment is likely to be needed again after a few years. Nevertheless, although bracken may be a nuisance to the hill farmer, aesthetically it adds welcome variety to the upland landscape.

Ecological succession and scrub colonization

In our climate, any patch of bare ground is likely to be quickly colonized by green plants. Whether this becomes grassland depends mainly on whether the area is grazed or mown and on the availability of seeds of woody plants. The first colonists are usually a miscellaneous assortment of weedy species, mainly broad-leaved herbs. Under favourable conditions a continuous turf can become established within a

When it is not intensively grazed, chalk grassland is rapidly colonized by shrubs. In Britain this happened after myxomatosis greatly reduced the rabbit population. Here the colonizing shrubs are hawthorn *(Crataegus monogyna)* with, in the background, silvery-white bushes of whitebeam *(Sorbus aria)*.

Right: Over many of the hills in northern Britain, particularly on damper and more acid soils, the grassland is very poor and is dominated by the mat-grass *Nardus stricta*. This type of grassland is encouraged by heavy sheep-grazing until it forms a uniform coat of pale green tussocks over the hill tops. Flowering period: June-August.

few years, though in its early stages it is likely to be poor in species. Provided there is no radical change in the character of the habitat, plant communities tend to become progressively richer in species with time as new colonists arrive. This is exemplified by the great diversity of species in many of the old traditional mowing meadows, or in uncultivated chalk and limestone pastures.

Grasses are, as we have seen, well adapted to withstand grazing, because their growing points are well protected close to soil level. In this respect they have a particular advantage over woody species which have their buds vulnerably placed at the tips of the shoots. In the absence of grazing, grasslands are rapidly colonized by scrub. On fertile agricultural grasslands the main colonist is usually hawthorn *(Crataegus monogyna)*, often with blackthorn *(Prunus spinosa)*, brambles *(Rubus fruticosus agg.)* and roses *(Rosa* species). On calcareous soils a wider range of species occur, including traveller's-joy *(Clematis vitalba)*, dogwood *(Cornus sanguinea)*, spindle *(Euonymus europaeus)*, juniper *(Juniperus communis)* (also found on various poor non-calcareous soils), wild privet *(Ligustrum vulgare)*, buckthorn *(Rhamnus catharticus)*, yew *(Taxus baccata)* and wayfaring tree *(Viburnum lantana)*. Elder *(Sambucus nigra)* is characteristic of nutrient-rich sites, such as those around old rabbit warrens. On acid soils in Britain, Ireland and western France, common gorse *(Ulex europaeus)* and bracken are important in the early stages of scrub colonization, either alone (followed by birch), or with brambles, roses, hawthorn and perhaps holly *(Ilex aquifolium)* or grey willow *(Salix cinerea)*. Given favourable soil, the seed of appropriate shrubs and trees, and little or no grazing, dense scrub can develop within a decade or two, and grassland may be replaced by woodland within half a century.

On poorer soils, or if some grazing continues, the process may take very much longer, and open scrub interspersed with grassland can persist for a considerable time before scrub eventually takes over. Quickly developed dense scrub usually contains very few species but old open scrub supports a characteristic range of species otherwise found mainly along hedgebanks and wood margins. These include agrimony *(Agrimonia eupatoria)*, lesser burdock *(Arctium minus)*, wild basil *(Clinopodium vulgare)*, cleavers *(Galium aparine)*, hedge bedstraw *(G. mollugo)*, ground-ivy *(Glechoma hederacea)*, several St. John's-worts *(Hypericum* species), common gromwell *(Lithospermum officinale)*, marjoram *(Origanum vulgare)*, wood sage *(Teucrium scorodonia)* and many others.

Renewed grazing will halt the spread of the scrub, and if it is heavy enough may leave nothing but a scattering of the bushes that have already grown tall and robust enough to escape browsing.

5
Heaths and moorlands

Less than a hundred years ago, heaths and moors occurred extensively along most of the Atlantic seaboard of Europe. This is still true of some countries of north-west Europe, but in others what was once an extensive habitat is now much reduced and fragmented. Nevertheless, the surviving heathlands and moors retain their charm and interest. Their charm is essentially that of a wide open landscape, sometimes with scattered trees and shrubs, sometimes without, but always dominated by low, shrubby heath plants, brown in winter but brilliant purple when they bloom late in summer. Their interest comes both from characteristic groupings of plants and animals, and also from the many uses to which heaths and moors have been put by man. Indeed, to a large extent, they owe their very existence to human influence. Over many generations, people have gained a livelihood from heaths and moors, and the imprint of this environment has been stamped on their local traditions, arts and ways of life. Heath and moor have in fact played an important role in the economy of western Europe.

Vegetation which is similar in appearance, though composed largely of different species, occurs in other parts of the world as well. The difference in Europe is that the extent of heath and moor has been greatly enlarged by human activity, creating ecosystems which, though made up of naturally-occurring plants and animals, owe their continued existence to various types of management.

There are no very precise definitions of the terms heath and moor and to some degree they are interchangeable. However, the Germanic word heath (*Heide* in German) probably referred originally to the tracts of this vegetation in lowland areas on acidic, sandy, freely-drained soils. These were widespread, for example, on the north German plain, where the dominant plant, *Calluna vulgaris*, was named *Heidekraut* (heather or ling in English) after the vegetation of which it was so characteristic.

Moorland is widespread on the hills of Britain. Here heather (*Calluna vulgaris*) and bracken (*Pteridium aquilinum*) cover a dry slope set amongst mires and a lake. The trees on the island show that the area lies below the tree-line, but current management techniques have excluded trees from the moor itself.

Botanically speaking, however, the word heath is generally used to denote all plant communities in which trees and large shrubs, if present at all, are sparse and scattered, while a dense canopy is formed, generally less than 1 m above the ground, by low, bushy plants with woody branches, their finer twigs clothed with very small, tough leaves, in most cases evergreen. These heath plants, belonging to the family Ericaceae, are sometimes accompanied by members of the pea family (Leguminosae), which are often spiny, such as species of gorse (Ulex) and the related genus *Genista*. Growing with the low shrubs are various herbs and grasses, and often a rich variety of mosses, liverworts and lichens. Where scattered trees do occur, they belong to species characteristic of neighbouring woodland on acid, nutrient-poor soils, such as Scots pine *(Pinus sylvestris)*, beech *(Fagus sylvatica)*, and species of birch *(Betula)* and oak *(Quercus)*. Juniper *(Juniperus communis)*, a shrub which may grow quite tall, is particularly characteristic of the heathlands of north-west Europe. Although by no means always present, where it does occur the small clumps or isolated bushes, ranging from tall, columnar to spreading, bushy forms, make a striking contribution to the landscape, particularly in southern Sweden, Denmark, north Germany and the Netherlands. In the heaths of more southern areas, for example in England and northern France, gorse *(Ulex europaeus)* is a common shrub.

The term heath is also applied to the vegetation of mountainsides and ridges, where low ericaceous shrubs may again be characteristic, usually in exposed places. The most important are the crowberry *(Empetrum nigrum)*, bearberry *(Arctostaphylos uva-ursi)* and trailing azalea *(Loiseleuria procumbens)*. These mountain heaths will be considered further in Chapter 6.

Moorland is also a rather general term but is usually applied to open, treeless vegetation at middle altitudes. Like the lowland heaths, moorland is often dominated by heather but it may also include grasslands, especially those characterized by purple moor-grass *(Molinia caerulea)* or mat-grass *(Nardus stricta)*. These moor-grasslands are discussed in Chapter 4.

Low and middle-altitude heaths and moorlands are best developed in areas where the climate is oceanic and where the soils are acid and poor. In north-west Europe their distribution is therefore very similar to that of the oceanic, western parts of the region, where there is relatively high rainfall (usually over 600 mm, well spread throughout the year but with a winter maximum), with cool summers and mild winters, giving a generally humid atmosphere.

Heaths are conveniently subdivided into dry heaths, which occur on freely-drained soils ranging from sands and gravels to various types of podsolic soils; and wet heaths, on

Low and middle altitude heaths and moorlands are restricted mainly to the western part of the region, where the oceanic climate features high rainfall, cool summers and mild winters.

The more continental heaths often have prominent bushes of juniper *(Juniperus communis)*, both in its tall, slender form and its wider bushy shape. The shorter vegetation is formed of heather *(Calluna vulgaris)*, here in flower and looking pale pink, and bright green crowberry *(Empetrum nigrum)*.

Below: In southern England and northern France, gorse *(Ulex europaeus)* forms extensive heaths on dry sandy soil. On hot days in late summer the bushes resound with sharp cracks as the seeds are forcibly ejected from the pods. Flowering period: March-June.

A dry heath with bell heather *(Erica cinerea)* in full flower, heather *(Calluna vulgaris)* and grey-green prostrate juniper *(Juniperus communis)* with its horizontally growing branches. Flowering period: July-September.

moist soils, usually rich in organic material and often peaty. Both types, but especially wet heaths, occur outside the heath area described above, but it is within this area that they are most widespread and best developed.

Dry heaths

The dry heath area is a large one and there is considerable geographical variation in the composition of its plant communities. Heather is one of the few plants distributed throughout the whole area and is the dominant species in a great majority of dry heaths. To a large extent it determines the appearance of heathland landscapes. Other widespread, though not quite so abundant plants, include the sedge *Carex pilulifera* and the yellow-flowered petty whin *(Genista anglica)*, which belongs to drier and less highly organic soils. Bracken *(Pteridium aquilinum)* is also common on heathland in places where the soil is freely-drained and not too strongly acid. It is a vigorous competitor and may spread into areas where heather is weak either because the plants are old, or because they have failed to regenerate effectively after fire. In these situations bracken may become dominant to the exclusion of heather.

Most of the plants of dry heaths are more restricted in their distribution and so give character to the communities of particular districts. For example, it is possible to make a distinction between communities of the more highly oceanic, western fringe of the heath area, and all the rest. Bell heather (*Erica cinerea*), producing its brilliant purple flowers from July onwards, before those of heather, is one of the most prominent plants throughout much of this strongly oceanic belt, while other characteristic species often found here are the sedge *Carex binervis* and the hard fern (*Blechnum spicant*). Towards the north, especially in south-west Norway and northern Scotland, juniper is generally present in a low-growing, prostrate (horizontal) form, together with a wide range of other attractive plants including the heath spotted orchid (*Dactylorhiza maculata*) and cat's foot (*Antennaria dioica*). Mosses and liverworts are often luxuriant, some of them such as *Rhacomitrium lanuginosum* and *Rhytidiadelphus loreus* being especially typical.

Farther south, in the coastal regions of Ireland, Wales, south-west England, north-west and northern France, the western gorse (*Ulex gallii*) becomes important and, when flowering in late summer, adds splashes of brilliant yellow to the generally colourful appearance of the heathland. In southern England, this plant tends to be replaced in heaths east of Dorset by its close relative, the dwarf gorse (*Ulex minor*), while in France (Normandy and Brittany) the two often occur together. These heaths often extend to the edge of sea cliffs where, because constantly exposed to wind and sea-spray, they form a type of low-growing, mat-like maritime vegetation (see Chapter 11).

These two small species of gorse are much the same height as heather and grow intimately mixed with it. The taller gorse (*Ulex europaeus*) is also common in heaths throughout north-west Europe and tends to form scattered thickets. In southern England and parts of northern France it becomes an integral member of the plant communities, often dominating extensive areas. Flowers may be seen at almost any time of year and when all the bushes are in bloom, the whole heath turns golden. The mixture of gorse and heather provides a habitat for the Dartford warbler (*Sylvia undata*), a bird which is confined to this type of heath in our region. In some districts broom (*Cytisus scoparius*) is also an important colonist.

There are other links between the heathland plants of southern England and those of northern France. One example is provided by the bent-grass *Agrostis curtisii*, which forms dense clumps of fine, hair-like leaves amongst heather on the sandy heaths in south-west England as well as in northern and western France. Another is the Cornish heath (*Erica vagans*), restricted in the British Isles to the Lizard Peninsula but occurring in western France from Brittany southwards, as well as in central France, the Pyrenees, northern Spain and Portugal. There are similar links between the flora of the west of Ireland and the oceanic heathlands of western France, as, for example, St Daboec's heath, (*Daboecia cantabrica*) and the Irish heath (*Erica erigena*), which grow on the more southerly heathlands extending from north-west France southwards into south-west France and northern Spain. Several other heaths such as *Erica scoparia* and the tree heath *E. arborea* are typical of these communities, which contain a rich variety of plants.

The types of heathland so far described belong mainly to the Atlantic fringe of the heath area. In districts sufficiently removed from the immediate influence of the sea for the climate to be less strongly oceanic, many of the characteristic species are different. Again, there are several different types—the northern (boreal) heaths and moors of southern Norway, south-west Sweden, Scotland, northern England and a few places in the Netherlands and northern Germany (especially on north-facing slopes); the subcontinental heaths of southern Sweden and countries around the southern shores of the Baltic; and the Dutch-German heaths.

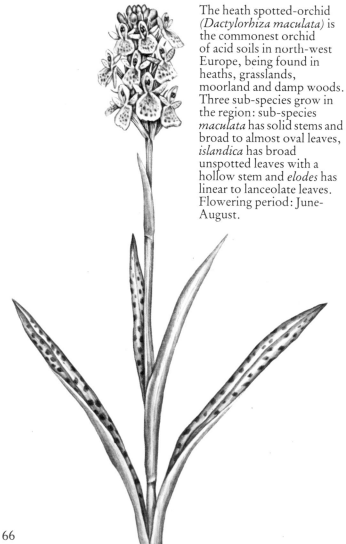

The heath spotted-orchid (*Dactylorhiza maculata*) is the commonest orchid of acid soils in north-west Europe, being found in heaths, grasslands, moorland and damp woods. Three sub-species grow in the region: sub-species *maculata* has solid stems and broad to almost oval leaves, *islandica* has broad unspotted leaves with a hollow stem and *elodes* has linear to lanceolate leaves. Flowering period: June-August.

St Daboec's heath *(Daboecia cantabrica)* is one of several species that grow only in Ireland, western France and the Iberian peninsula. It is usually found in dry heaths where it can be distinguished from the other heathers by its larger flowers, which have their parts arranged in fours rather than the usual fives. Flowering period: July-September.

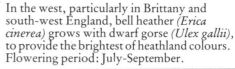

In the west, particularly in Brittany and south-west England, bell heather *(Erica cinerea)* grows with dwarf gorse *(Ulex gallii)*, to provide the brightest of heathland colours. Flowering period: July-September.

Catsfoot *(Antennaria dioica)* is a small perennial with a creeping woody stock from which grow stolons. The undersides of the leaves are white and woolly; the flowering shoots are short, with 2 to 8 stalked heads. It is found on heaths, dry pastures and dry slopes chiefly in the mountains or more northerly lowland areas. Flowering period: June-July.

In the northern heaths, from the Netherlands to southern Norway and in the northern half of the British Isles, heather is perhaps at its most vigorous, and may be accompanied by plants such as bilberry *(Vaccinium myrtillus)*, cowberry *(V. vitis-idaea)* and crowberry *(Empetrum nigrum)*. These are all plants with a northern and montane type of distribution, ranging from lowland heaths to the middle-altitude moorlands of the British Isles and Scandinavia. Also frequent in these northern heaths are plants such as tormentil *(Potentilla erecta)* with its small, bright yellow flowers; chickweed wintergreen *(Trientalis europaea)* with pure white, star-shaped flowers; milkwort *(Polygala serpyllifolia)*, whose flowers may be red, purple, blue or white; lesser twayblade *(Listera cordata)*, a diminutive and inconspicuous orchid growing beneath heather bushes; heath bedstraw *(Galium saxatile)*, a creeping plant with small white flowers; wavy hair-grass *(Deschampsia flexuosa)* and the clubmoss *Lycopodium clavatum*. Mosses are often luxuriant, notably *Pleurozium schreberi*, *Hylocomium splendens* and *Hypnum cupressiforme*. On drier ground lichens become abundant, particularly the conspicuous white, much branched *Cladonia impexa* or the robust, greenish-brown *Cetraria islandica*.

Where the soils have a thick surface layer of acid, raw humus the variety of species is not great. On more mineral

Crowberry *(Empetrum nigrum)* has very small pinkish or purplish flowers, only 1 to 2mm across; these are replaced in the autumn by small black fruits, about 5mm in diameter. The edges of its bright green leaves are bent back so that the lower surface is visible only as a white line. Flowering period: May-June.

soils, however, where there is a better supply of plant nutrients, a somewhat richer community may develop with more grasses, for example *Danthonia decumbens*, common bent *(Agrostis capillaris)* or sheep's-fescue *(Festuca ovina)*, and flowering plants such as harebell *(Campanula rotundifolia)*, bird's-foot-trefoil *(Lotus corniculatus)*, ribwort plantain *(Plantago lanceolata)*, fairy flax *(Linum catharticum)* and thyme *(Thymus praecox)*.

A form of this herb-rich heath community contains bearberry *(Arctostaphylos uva-ursi)*, another mainly boreal plant, together with certain characteristic species including slender St John's wort *(Hypericum pulchrum)*, petty whin and bitter vetch *(Lathyrus montanus)*. This readily recognizable group of plants is found in south-west Norway, parts of Denmark, and the central uplands and north-east of Scotland (where the wintergreen *Pyrola media* is a frequent member of the community). A related type of heath occurs in south-west Sweden. Here there are some differences in the plant communities, for example petty whin is replaced by the hairy greenweed *(Genista pilosa)*.

The crowberry, though widespread, tends to be especially prominent on both sides of the North Sea, as far south as the Netherlands, where it forms dense mats, excluding most other plants. In the heathlands of southern Sweden and countries surrounding the southern part of the Baltic, where

the climate is subcontinental, plants with oceanic requirements, such as bell heather and hard fern, are absent, but are replaced by others, such as *Arnica montana*, which have a more continental distribution.

The Dutch-German heaths form a group which is best developed in the north German plain, one example being the famous Lüneburger Heide. They also occur in the Netherlands, Belgium and a few places in southern England. None of the northern-montane plants are found here; instead there are species such as hairy greenweed, dyer's greenweed *(G. tinctoria)* and *G. germanica*, whose distributions extend southwards into the lowlands of central and southern Europe. Another very characteristic southern plant is the parasitic dodder *(Cuscuta epithymum)*, with thin red stems which twine around the branches of heather and gorse, sending suckers into the tissues. Grasses are generally prominent in these heaths, but vegetation cover is seldom complete on the freely drained sandy soils. This permits a wide variety of lichens to grow, but, with the notable exception of *Hypnum cupressiforme*, mosses are less common.

Despite all this variation, heather remains the chief plant of the drier heaths of western Europe. Although others, such as wavy hair-grass or bell heather, may be quicker to colonize bare areas, heather almost invariably invades and eventually

Left: Whilst harebells *(Campanula rotundifolia)* are usually found in grasslands, they are quite common in heaths on richer soils. The lowest leaves are round, providing the latin name *rotundifolia*; those on the flowering stems are long and narrow. Flowering period: July-September.

The common tormentil *(Potentilla erecta)* is one of the commonest herbs found in heathlands. Its small yellow flowers have four petals and sepals, distinguishing them from most other cinquefoils, which have five. Flowering period: June-September.

The hairy greenweed *(Genista pilosa)* is characteristic of the eastern, more continental heaths. The undersides of its leaves are covered with closely pressed hairs which give them a greyish colour. Unlike the petty whin *(Genista anglica)*, the hairy greenweed has no spines on its stem. Flowering period: May-June.

overtops the rest. Not surprisingly, there are many animals that eat heather, including numerous insects as well as the larger grazing mammals. Among the more conspicuous of the insects are the caterpillars of the emperor moth *(Saturnia pavonia)* and the northern eggar ('woolly bear' caterpillars; *Lasiocampus quercus* var. *callunae)*. But the animal which does most damage is the heather beetle *(Lochmaea suturalis)*. Both larvae and adults feed on heather shoots and in parts of the heath area, especially the Netherlands, northern Germany and, more locally, in the British Isles, periodic outbreaks may kill the heather either in patches or more continuously over quite wide areas.

This is just one of many reasons why there are gaps of varying size in the heather canopy; others are fire, trampling by grazing animals or people, passage of vehicles or merely the death of old heather plants. Whatever the cause, gaps provide opportunities for colonists. On the drier soils the first are often lichens, mainly species of *Cladonia*, some with brown or brilliant red spots where the spores are formed. Mosses may also be quick to appear, as, for example the short *Polytrichum piliferum* with fine white hair-points at the tips of its leaves, *Ceratodon purpureus*, or on moister peaty surfaces *Leptodontium flexifolium*, *Campylopus flexuosus* and other species of *Campylopus* including *C. introflexus*. *C. introflexus* is an attractive species widespread in mainland

Europe but only recently introduced into Britain, where it has spread with great rapidity as a colonist of disturbed peaty ground. These species are often followed by slightly taller mosses such as *Pohlia nutans* or *Dicranum scoparium*, and then by the mat-forming species *Hypnum cupressiforme* and *Pleurozium schreberi*.

On the whole, heathland vegetation is composed of perennial plants. However, gaps in the vegetation provide opportunities for colonization by some annuals or short-lived perennials, as for example shepherd's cress *(Teesdalia nudicaulis)*, which grows on sandy soils and forms a neat rosette of leaves, from the centre of which comes a branched flower stalk with small white flowers in April or May. Other opportunists which may persist for several years include sheep's sorrel *(Rumex acetosella)*, common speedwell *(Veronica officinalis)* and common violet *(Viola riviniana)*.

Wet heaths

Wet heaths develop wherever drainage is impeded, whether because of the nature of the soil or, more usually, for topographical reasons. They may occur either in wet hollows of dry heathland or as extensive wet areas which have developed on level ground where the water-table is near the surface. Heather may survive in wet-heath vegetation, but it does not grow so vigorously. The most characteristic species is the cross-leaved heath *(Erica tetralix)* which has larger, bright pink, bell-shaped flowers. Bell heather, however, is absent. As the soil becomes wetter, *Sphagnum* and other mosses such as the whitish cushion-forming *Leucobryum glaucum* or the dark green *Polytrichum commune* become more prominent and heather is gradually eliminated. Creeping willow *(Salix repens)* and the fragrant bog myrtle *(Myrica gale)* join the ranks of the low shrubs, and there are varying numbers of grasses, sedges and rushes such as purple moor-grass, the cottongrass *Eriophorum vaginatum*, the rush *Juncus squarrosus* and deergrass *(Scirpus cespitosus)*. A variety of other attractive plants may occur, including the blue-flowered devil's-bit scabious *(Succisa pratensis)*, the bright pink lousewort *Pedicularis sylvatica*, the yellow bog asphodel *(Narthecium ossifragum)*, and the beautiful white grass-of-Parnassus *(Parnassia palustris)*. The insectivorous plants sundew *(Drosera rotundifolia)* and common butterwort *(Pinguicula vulgaris)* may be found growing amongst *Sphagnum* or other mosses.

Many of these species are widespread, and on the whole the composition of wet heath varies less than that of the dry heath communities. Some plants of wet heath, however, are more restricted in their distribution and are characteristic of particular districts. Examples of these are the blue-flowered marsh gentian *(Gentiana pneumonanthe)*, one of the finest

Arnica montana is a plant chiefly of central and southern Europe but within our region it occurs in the more continental heaths, particularly around the Baltic Sea. It is easily recognized by its hairy, undivided, leaves and its few large, yellow flower heads. Flowering period: May-June.

Cladonia macilenta, a lichen from a genus frequently found on the ground between heather bushes on heaths and moorlands. The brown or brilliant red spots often seen on these lichens mark the areas where reproductive spores are found.

On heather and gorse a tangled mass of reddish, thread-like stems can often be found, attached at intervals to the host plants. This is the dodder *(Cuscuta epithymum)*, a parasite deriving all its food from the plants on which it grows. Its pinkish flowers are borne in small dense heads at intervals up the leafless stems. Flowering period: July–September.

The common speedwell *(Veronica officinalis)* is often found in the more open areas of heath, where gaps between the bushes allow smaller plants to grow. Another perennial speedwell likely to be found in the same situations is the thyme-leaved speedwell *(V. serpyllifolia)*. It can be distinguished from the common speedwell by its flowers which appear at the end of the stem instead of in the leaf axils. Flowering period: May–August.

plants of wet heaths in southern England, the Netherlands and other countries of the central part of the heath area; *Ledum palustre*, a shrub of more continental districts; and the Dorset heath *(Erica ciliaris)*, which again links south-west England with northern France.

As on dry heaths, there are plants that appear in gaps or damp ruts and hollows. Among these are the annuals allseed *(Radiola linoides)* and yellow centaury *(Cicendia filiformis)*, which is allied to the gentians and occurs in western Europe from Denmark to Spain. In the British Isles it is largely confined to southern England, south Wales and south-western Ireland. Also rather rare but found in similar habitats is the marsh clubmoss *(Lycopodium inundatum)*.

Origins, use and management

Heaths and moorlands are, by definition, largely devoid of trees. While it is relatively easy to account for the absence of trees from the harsh environment of mountain dwarf heaths and from wet heath—presumably as a result of waterlogging—it is less easy to explain why they do not grow on most dry heaths.

In some cases, dry heath is a temporary, successional stage

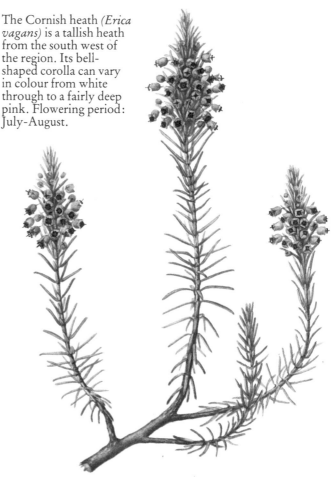

The Cornish heath *(Erica vagans)* is a tallish heath from the south west of the region. Its bell-shaped corolla can vary in colour from white through to a fairly deep pink. Flowering period: July–August.

The marsh gentian *(Gentiana pneumonanthe)* is one of the most striking plants found in the wet heaths. Unfortunately it is declining rapidly throughout Europe as the areas where it grows are drained for agricultural purposes, and it is now quite rare. Flowering period: August-September.

The lousewort *(Pedicularis sylvatica)* is partly parasitic on the plants among which it grows. It is found on damp heaths and in bogs and marshes throughout the region. Flowering period: April-July.

Many of the lowland heaths in Europe are the result of man's activities. These Megalithic standing stones, set in a heath of western gorse *(Ulex gallii)* and bell heather *(Erica cinerea)* show how long human influence has been important in these habitats.

not yet colonized by taller plants. An example is dune heath on acid sand-dunes. As the surface of the sand is stabilized, first by marram grass *(Ammophila arenaria)* and then by mosses, lichens, rosette or creeping herbs and turf-forming grasses, heath plants such as heather, bell heather, or, towards the north, crowberry, begin to appear. These form a dune heath in which they are associated with typical sand-dune plants such as sand sedge *(Carex arenaria)*. The sand-dune plants gradually disappear and, in the course of time, if seed parents of tall shrubs or trees are available in the neighbourhood, the heath may be replaced by scrub and eventually woodland.

Particularly severe climatic conditions may exclude trees in some places, as, for example, on the flat or gently sloping

development of woodland. This was suggested for parts of the glacial outwash plains of Jutland. Graebner, one of the earlier German writers on heathland ecology, held the view that continued development of the podzols under forests on very poor sandy soils (as in parts of the north German plain) would lead to such impoverishment of the nutrient supply in the rooting region that the forest would fail to regenerate, and would give place to heath. However, it seems that these views, like those on climatic change, could only apply to a few extreme cases.

A third argument, put forward by Tansley with respect to heaths in south-east England, is that heathland which developed as a temporary phase in the recolonization of land covered by ice during the glacial periods was quickly occupied by man, who prevented tree colonization. However, there is now clear evidence from pollen analysis that, over virtually the whole of the heath area, heaths and moorland were formerly occupied by forest.

The change from forest to heath evidently took place at many different times in the past, beginning in some areas as early as the Neolithic period and gathering momentum in the Bronze Age (from about 1700 BC) and Iron Age (from 500 BC to Roman times). The same trend can be seen in the historical period from about AD 800 right up to the nineteenth century. In the great majority of cases, the evidence of vegetational change is associated with signs of human activity, including the pollen of weeds and cereals which indicate that the ground must have been used temporarily for cultivation.

It seems certain, therefore, that man was the chief agent in changing forest to heath and moorland. When the land was used for cultivation, it often quickly became unsuitable for crops as its fertility declined. Such land was then available for re-invasion by trees but more often it was given over to grazing animals, when it became grassland or heath. On acid soils, heath plants such as heather and bilberry were already present as an understorey or in clearings and glades in the rather open forest, so they were easily able to spread into the cleared land. The whole of the heath area lies within the natural distribution limits of heather, which is an effective colonist of newly cleared areas because of the vast numbers of very small, light seeds it produces every year.

On these soils, low in nutrient content and not very productive, heather proved to be a valuable grazing plant, providing nutritious shoots, available in winter as well as in summer. The heathlands therefore acquired an important use as pasture for cattle and sheep, being especially valuable for winter grazing although much used in summer as well. To some extent the herbivores themselves prevented the return of trees, and, by continually removing the young shoots, kept the heather in a vigorous, productive condition.

There is always a tendency, however, for a perennial shrub

tops of exposed sea cliffs where maritime heath develops. But over most of the heath area, the climate is much more moderate. One explanation for the absence of trees was that a change in climate towards cooler and wetter conditions around 500 BC may have permitted heath to spread at the expense of forest. While this may have been a contributory factor in some of the more northerly heathland areas, there does not seem to be any climatic feature which would inhibit the growth of trees such as pine and birch in parts of Scotland and Scandinavia, or oak and beech farther south. Indeed, heath and moorland often border woodland and these trees, together with various shrubs, may sometimes be seen invading heath.

Another theory is that soil conditions might prevent the

such as heather to become tall and woody, so that its grazing value declines. From earliest times, therefore, some form of management additional to grazing animals was required. Fire proved an effective, cheap and easy way to remove the old woody parts of the vegetation; moreover heather responds remarkably well to burning. So long as the plants are not too old when burned, a cluster of shoots will grow from the stem base, which generally remains alive when most of the rest is destroyed. In this way, a new, vigorous, even-aged stand of heather rapidly replaces the ageing plants. Even when such re-growth is less successful, heather will eventually return as seedlings establish themselves, though this is a slower process.

At first, fire was probably used only at irregular intervals, but from the late eighteenth century, particularly in the British Isles, heathlands were increasingly devoted to sheep alone and to maintain the heather in its most productive condition it became necessary to burn at regular intervals of about ten to twelve years. It is also common practice to burn gorse where it forms impenetrable thickets on some heathlands, but, like heather, this plant will grow again from the stem bases and it is not possible to control it by means of fire alone.

The development of large tracts of moorland at middle altitudes in the hills of the British Isles also led to a great increase in the populations of the native red grouse (*Lagopus lagopus scoticus*), which feeds mainly on heather. The presence of grouse, together with the red deer (*Cervus elaphus*), attracted sportsmen to the moors and when the profitability of hill sheep began to decline, a welcome new source of income was available for landowners in the form of rent from shooting-tenants. Little change in the system of management was needed, because grouse depend on the same food as hill sheep. However, during the breeding season, pairs of grouse establish territories which must contain both young heather for feeding and older stands for shelter and concealment of the nest. It is important, therefore, to ensure that fires are confined to small patches or strips, creating a mosaic of stands at different stages of regeneration. This produces the familiar patchwork appearance of well-managed grouse moors.

Where the terrain was gentle and cultivation relatively easy, as on the plains of Jutland, heathland was often used for growing crops. Usually the heath was cleared by burning before it was ploughed, but although nutrients released from the ash acted to some extent as a fertilizer the poor soils would support little but rye and buckwheat. After a few harvests the ground was exhausted and had to be abandoned for as long as ten to twenty years, allowing the heath to recover. In this way, although crops were taken at intervals, the heathland landscape was retained.

Trees such as the silver birch (*Betula verrucosa*) in the background here are usually prevented from colonizing heathland by grazing animals. Sheep or rabbits nibble the tender shoots of the seedling trees and prevent them from maturing.

A different system of management evolved in northern Germany, the Netherlands and Belgium, in a belt extending roughly from Antwerp to Hamburg. Here the surface humus, litter and vegetation was stripped from areas of heathland in the form of sods. These were used to provide bedding in barns where sheep, which grazed the heath during the daytime, were kept at night. In this way sheep manure was added to the humus, which was then used to improve the poor sandy soils around farms and villages, giving rise to productive dark-coloured *plaggensoils*. The heathlands, periodically denuded of their humus layers, regenerated slowly, usually going through a phase of lichen colonization before heather seedlings reappeared, with grasses and herbs such as *Danthonia decumbens*, common bent, *Carex pilulifera* and tormentil. It has been estimated that some heaths were cut between ten and fifty times, at intervals of ten to twenty years. Again, this type of land-use helped to perpetuate the heathlands.

Present changes and future prospects

Throughout most of western Europe heathland is no longer of economic importance. As agricultural production on better land has intensified, the extensive grazing systems, primitive forms of cultivation and sod-cutting in these marginal areas have gradually been abandoned. The major exception to this general trend is found in northern England

Old heather makes poor grazing for sheep and provides little food for grouse. It is often burned to remove the old wood and promote the growth of vigorous young stems from the stumps.

The reason for this is that heathland vegetation has been maintained in the past by management practices which have now fallen into disuse, and as a result the plant communities are not stable, but subject to relatively rapid change. Such change may be towards scrub or woodland, or, if trees do not invade, ageing stands of heather may die out simultaneously over quite wide areas giving place, for example, to grassland dominated on the drier soils by wavy hair-grass or in wetter places by purple moor-grass.

Active management is therefore needed to conserve heathland. In some places, such as certain reserves in Denmark and on the Lüneburger Heide in Germany, this takes the form of continuing traditional grazing systems or re-introducing grazing animals (sheep or cattle) on an experimental basis. It is often difficult and expensive, however, to maintain a heathland reserve by these means. A return to regular burning is another possibility, and this would certainly keep the heather stands in a young and vigorous condition, largely preventing invasion by other plants. This would preserve the heathland landscape but would encourage the dominance of heather and tend to eliminate many other plant species, probably also reducing the diversity of animals. For purposes of nature conservation, what is required is not dense, even-aged stands of heather, but patchy, uneven-aged stands with many gaps which allow a variety of other plants to flourish as well. Frequent burning of very small patches may be the answer but this is often both time-consuming and difficult. An alternative is to avoid burning, at least for periods of twenty to thirty years, long enough to allow the heather to become old and the stand uneven in age. This interval would generally be too long to prevent trees and shrubs from colonizing and hand-cutting would be necessary.

A further possibility, at present being tried in a number of places, is mowing. Heather usually regenerates as well, if not better, after mowing as after burning. New machinery is available which mows heather fairly close to ground level, and chops up the branches into fragments which do not prevent new plants from growing. Mowing can be carried out easily on a small scale in scattered patches, and may prove to be a useful and acceptable means of rejuvenating heather stands in nature reserves.

Whatever method is adopted, it is clear that for conservation purposes active management is needed to prevent succession to woodland from taking place, with the loss of important examples of the various communities of plants and animals. Heaths and moorland have for long been part of the human environment of western Europe and are both aesthetically satisfying and scientifically interesting. The effort required to ensure survival of representative examples is surely well worth while.

and Scotland where heath and moor continue to be used for free-range sheep grazing or for sporting purposes and as a result extensive tracts remain. Elsewhere, the area of heathland has declined spectacularly during the past sixty to a hundred years. In south-west Sweden, Denmark and northern Germany heathland constituted a major element in the landscape up to the latter part of the nineteenth century; today almost the only examples surviving are those protected as nature reserves. In Sweden most of the former heathland has been afforested and some converted to arable land. Much of the Danish heathland has been brought under the plough, largely through the influence of the Danish Heath Society, which has provided the necessary financial and technical support to encourage farmers to convert heath into good quality farmland by the use of fertilizers and special machinery. In Germany, the Netherlands, Belgium and southern England heaths have widely given place to coniferous plantations, arable land and improved grassland, or have disappeared beneath roads and buildings.

In these ways, a very distinctive element of the landscape of western Europe, together with its typical plants and animals, is being reduced almost to extinction. Effective conservation of the best surviving fragments is therefore a matter of urgency. Reserves incorporating areas of heath and moor have been set up in all the countries concerned, but there are difficulties in developing effective systems of management.

6
The high mountains

This chapter is concerned with the variety of plant communities which occur in the mountains of north-west Europe above the natural tree-line. This restricts it to the mountains of the British Isles, Faeroes, Iceland and Fennoscandia. There has been some argument about how to recognize the tree-line, but it is usually taken to be the upper limit of more or less continuous woodland, although there may be isolated trees above this point. These have usually grown from seed blown up from trees lower down and they do not normally succeed in reproducing themselves. The natural tree-line in north-west Europe is almost invariably formed by downy birch *(Betula pubescens)* and the birch woods below this line are referred to as the subalpine zone.

The tree-line

With increasing altitude the temperature falls at a fairly constant rate known as the lapse-rate. During the summer this is about 0.6°C per 100m. The tree-line represents the altitude at which trees are no longer able to grow and it is likely that this occurs when increasing cold reduces the growing season below a certain critical length. One important effect of the short growing season is that trees are unable to harden their current year's growth sufficiently to withstand the low winter temperatures. It is likely that early spring, when there are still heavy night-frosts, is a particularly critical period as the spring sunshine reduces the hardiness of the shoots. Wind also plays a very important role, especially in inhibiting or preventing tree-growth in exposed situations such as ridges. This may be due to physical damage, to excessive loss of water by frozen tissues, and to reduced temperatures in the tips of the growing shoots.

The altitude of the tree-line varies considerably, especially with latitude and the oceanicity of the climate. In the Alps, its maximum altitude is about 2600m; in central Norway it falls to about 1200m, while north of the Arctic Circle it descends

An early summer scene in western Norway. The dense subalpine birch woods ascend to about 800m and then give way to the dwarf shrub and grassland communities of the alpine zone, still largely snow-covered. Around the riverside farms, the trees have been felled to create hay meadows.

below 500m. This progressive lowering is due to the general changes in climate with latitude brought about by the decreasing intensity of solar radiation and the corresponding reduction in the growing season. The northernmost parts of Fennoscandia are very close to the latitudinal limit for tree growth, which follows fairly closely the 10°C mean July isotherm. Both the latitudinal tree-line and this isotherm are commonly used to define the southern limit of the Arctic.

The variation from east to west is just as impressive and can be seen across the whole region: for example, the highest tree-line in Fennoscandia is just over 1200m, in the Jotunheimen; in Scotland, though 500km to the south, it is 640m in the Cairngorms, and is of pine, not birch. Further north and west, in Iceland, birch woods are largely confined to below 300m; this compares with about 800m at the same latitude in Sweden. Even within these countries the tree-line is highest in the more continental areas in the east, which have relatively high sunshine and low rainfall. Along the whole of the western coast of Fennoscandia the tree-line 80km inland is twice as high as it is on the coast and in Scotland the birch tree-line falls from 610m in the east to about 300m in the north-west.

These changes are related to the increasing oceanicity of the climate towards the west, particularly the increased cloud and precipitation and the lower summer temperatures. The annual and daily ranges are also smaller than in continental areas. As a result, the same increase in altitude produces a greater reduction in the growing season, so lowering the upper limit at which trees can grow.

The tree-line may also be influenced by topography; for example, it is usually lower on a lower, isolated mountain range than on a higher, or larger one. This may be because at the same altitude lower, smaller ranges are windier than higher, larger ones. This effect of topography is illustrated by the profile of the tree-line across central Norway: it is 400m higher in the Jotunheimen than on the Swedish border much farther east. Similarly, the isolated, small mountain areas of northern Finland, although farther from the coast, have lower tree-lines than the larger mountain areas to the west.

In many areas, particularly in Britain and Iceland, it is now extremely difficult to determine the natural tree-line. According to the Icelandic Sagas, at the time Iceland was colonized, about a thousand years ago, there were extensive lowland birch forests, but their use for fuel and intensive grazing, chiefly by sheep, has resulted in catastrophic deforestation which, in many areas, is complete. A similar process has occurred in Britain: the extensive pine forests in the Scottish Highlands have been largely destroyed since the Middle Ages and replaced by moorlands and grasslands. Even in northern Fennoscandia there is evidence of at least local lowering of the natural tree-line by the Lapps whose summer camps are usually situated at or close to the upper limit of tree growth. In the extreme north, the Varanger Peninsula is often said to lie north of the latitudinal tree-line and therefore in the Arctic. Certainly much of it is a rolling treeless plateau, between 200 and 300m above sea level and mostly covered with mountain crowberry (*Empetrum nigrum* subsp. *hermaphroditum*) and lichen heaths, but this is the result of deforestation. There are still a few birch woods on the south-west coast and scattered trees on the north coast.

The mountain climate

The variation of the tree-line is of course only a reflection of the way in which the mountain climate varies, particularly with latitude and oceanicity. Meteorological data for mountain sites are scarce, but figures from oceanic and continental stations, all within 300m of the tree-line, show considerable differences in precipitation and winter temperature. The oceanic stations have a much higher precipitation and a warmer winter minimum temperature than do the continental stations, but the differences in summer temperature are less striking though very significant, continental stations being generally warmer and sunnier. For example, Abisko, in northern Sweden, with a July mean of 11°C, is about 2°C warmer than an equivalent altitude on the coast. It would be warmer still were it not for the presence nearby of the large, cold lake Torneträsk.

With increasing altitude above the tree-line, the vegetation continues to change and it is possible to recognize three main altitudinal zones, or belts. These are the lower, middle and upper alpine zones. Like the tree-line, the boundaries between them are primarily determined by climate. The lower alpine zone, occurring immediately above the tree-line, usually consists of dwarf-shrub heath and may extend through an altitudinal range of up to 500m in Fennoscandia, 400m in Iceland and 300m in Scotland. Above this is the middle alpine zone, often characterized by an open grassy heath. Finally, the upper alpine zone extends on the highest mountains into the region of permanent snow and ice. Because of the severe conditions, this zone supports only a few, highly adapted higher plants but many species of lichens, mosses and liverworts grow there. Like the tree-line, these zones are lower in oceanic areas and also narrower.

No mountains in the British Isles reach the upper alpine zone although summer on the summit of Ben Nevis (1321m) is not far short of upper-alpine conditions. The summit has only five months with a mean temperature above zero; the mean for July is only 5.4°C, the same as at 1600m, the beginning of the upper alpine zone, in the mountains of Rondane in eastern Norway. Ben Nevis is a good illustration

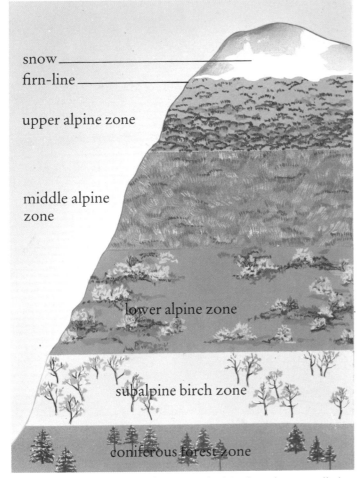

On mountains, vegetation changes with altitude and can usually be divided into fairly distinct zones. The lowest is usually the coniferous forest zone with above, a zone of subalpine birch. The lower alpine zone is characterized by heaths and the middle alpine by grasses and sedges. In the upper alpine zone, plant cover is very sparse; snow-lie increases and above the firn-line it persists throughout the year.

Screes provide such unstable habitats that plants colonize only with difficulty. One of the first to be found on acid rocks is the parsley-fern (*Cryptogramma crispa*).

of a mountain with an extremely oceanic mountain climate, having an average wind speed of almost 50 km per hour, only 750 hours of sunshine a year, 220 wet days and an annual precipitation of 4250 mm.

Soils and solifluction

Apart from the direct effects of climate, including that of snow cover, the most important factors influencing the vegetation and distribution of individual mountain species are those concerned with the soil. The harsh climate causes active erosion and the soils are therefore often unstable, with rocks progressively breaking down into smaller fragments. Many montane soils are unstructured and unstratified, usually with little organic matter and a high proportion of rock fragments. This is most dramatically seen below cliffs where there may be extremely unstable screes with no or only a few plants, for example parsley fern (*Cryptogramma crispa*).

A major cause of soil instability is solifluction. This is a term used to describe the effects of the alternate expansion and contraction of water in the soil as it freezes and thaws. The term should, strictly speaking, be limited to one type, found on slopes where the whole mass of soil, soaked with water, gradually creeps down the mountainside in a series of waves. The greatest disturbance of the soil is along the forward edge which may be up to half a metre high. On flat ground, frost-heaving may produce low, dome-shaped polygons and as the soil particles are gradually sorted, finer material accumulates in the centre and the larger stones, often arranged vertically, form the perimeter. These polygons may be relatively small or, in the most extreme conditions, up to several metres across. Inactive 'fossil' polygons may be found on lower summits, as in Britain, having been formed in the past when conditions were more severe. As the angle of slope increases, the polygons become progressively elongated downhill so that stone stripes of large stones are formed, separated by broader bands of fine soil. Frost-heaving may cause so much disturbance and root damage that in extreme conditions no plants can survive. Where it is less active, plants may be able to colonize the areas where the perimeters of the polygons meet, leaving the more disturbed centres open.

Where plants are able to colonize these soils, humus may accumulate and there may be a gradual stabilization, so that a structured, layered soil develops. As the amount of humus increases, the upper soil layers become more acidic, partly because they become insulated from the bedrock, which is the major source of the mineral nutrients, and partly because the nutrients present are washed or leached out by the rain.

Since different species vary in their range of nutrient

The rock speedwell (Veronica fruticans) is one of the most colourful plants of the drier, more base-rich habitats of the middle alpine zone. Flowering period: July–August.

The alpine forget-me-not (Myosotis alpestris) is found mainly in the Alps, Carpathians and surrounding mountains, but has northerly outposts on two mountains in Britain. Flowering period: July–September.

requirements, the mineral- or base-status of the soil is clearly an important factor in governing the distribution of species and of different types of vegetation. As mentioned in Chapter 1, the most important factor in determining the base-status of soils is the geology of the underlying rock. Rocks such as granite, gneisses and many sandstones contain relatively small amounts of calcium and magnesium and so give rise to soils which are acidic and base-poor. By contrast, rocks such as limestones, calcareous schists and basalts give base-rich soils which range from neutral to moderately alkaline. The base-status may also be improved by flushing. This is a localized concentration of nutrients and is brought about by two different processes, one dry, the other wet. Dry flushes occur where the soil is enriched by the accumulation of fresh, unweathered rock-fragments, as, for example, in the lower parts of a gully. Wet flushes are where enriched water percolates through or trickles over the soil as, for example, below spring lines. The effects of flushing clearly depend on the nature of the rock fragments or the rock through which the water has percolated. If this is acidic, the flushes will still be relatively base-poor; if the rocks are calcareous, the flushes will be base-rich. In most mountain areas in north-west Europe high precipitation leaches many essential nutrients from the soil and consequently any degree of flushing is important in providing habitats where plants that require the more base-rich soils can survive.

It is well known that the majority of mountain plants, especially those classed as 'alpines' by gardeners, prefer base-rich soils. This is why such sites are actively sought out by alpine enthusiasts and the best areas are internationally famous. Two such areas in Fennoscandia are the Dovrefjell, in eastern Norway, and the Abisko area in northernmost Sweden. Many mountain plants, mostly calcicoles, are confined to these two areas and to similar areas in central Norway and the north; the significance of this will be discussed at the end of this chapter. Examples of such bicentric species are Rhododendron lapponicum and Saxifraga hieracifolia; others are unicentric, occurring in either the southern or the northern area. Examples are the louseworts Pedicularis oederi from the south and P. flammea, P. hirsuta and the ericaceous shrub Cassiope tetragona from the north. In Scotland, Ben Lawers and the surrounding mountains, with their large outcrops of calcareous mica-schists, have the richest mountain flora in Britain. Some of the rarest British plants found there, such as the alpine forget-me-not (Myosotis alpestris) and the beautiful rock speedwell (Veronica fruticans) grow elsewhere in the central Scottish mountains, but Ben Lawers is the only locality in Britain for the sedge Carex microglochin. Similarly in England, the Teesdale area in the northern Pennines

Rhododendron lapponicum grows on calcareous soils in the lower alpine heaths and on stony slopes of the mountains of Fennoscandia. It grows very low to the ground and has brownish scales on its stems and leaves. Flowering period: June-July.

The mountain avens *(Dryas octopetala)* is especially characteristic of base-rich areas on mountains, where it can form extensive heaths. Flowering period: June-July.

harbours a number of mountain plants, many of which are rare and local, and most of which grow on the outcrops of metamorphosed 'sugar' limestone. They include spring gentian *(Gentiana verna)*, mountain avens *(Dryas octopetala)*, the grass *Alopecurus alpinus* and the inconspicuous sandwort *Minuartia stricta*, which is found nowhere else in Britain.

Topography, aspect and snow-lie

Mountains by their very nature create a variety of contrasted habitats. Their aspect and the angle of their slope are often of crucial importance in determining their vegetation. South-facing slopes will always receive more sunlight, both in number of hours and intensity than those facing north and will therefore be both warmer and drier. The more northerly the latitude the more important is the warming of south-facing slopes because of the lower angle of the sun. North-facing slopes often receive no direct sunlight in the winter months and little in summer, and in deep gullies no direct sunlight may ever penetrate. These sites have lower air and soil temperatures, higher humidity and damper soils.

Many mountain plants flourish only within a relatively narrow temperature range and a species characteristic of south-facing slopes in the middle and upper alpine zones may be found at lower altitudes on north-facing slopes, especially in gullies and on cliff-ledges. The maximum summer temperature appears to be an important factor affecting the distribution of many species, since their distributions are closely correlated with a particular isotherm. One example is roseroot *(Rhodiola rosea)*. The precise significance of this is uncertain and no doubt varies from species to species. Certainly several plants are able to tolerate appreciably higher temperatures in cultivation.

Another effect of aspect, and an extremely important one, is on snow-lie. Snow accumulates on the leeward side of ridges and in depressions and gullies. North- and east-facing slopes and gullies will naturally retain their snow longest and with increasing altitude permanent snow-patches may occur. In general, snow has two opposing effects. On the one hand, in winter, it forms a layer over the plants, protecting them both from extreme low temperatures and, just as important, from the severe abrasive force of strong winds carrying ice particles which cause damage, particularly to resting buds. On the other hand, the deeper the snow, for example in hollows, the later plants will emerge in the spring and the shorter their growing season will be. For this reason the vegetation of late snow-patch areas, often called snow-beds, is usually distinctive and arranged in concentric zones depending on the length of snow-lie. Since the proportion of

Many heaths of the low alpine zone, just above the tree line, are largely composed of the deciduous bearberry *(Arctostaphylos alpinus)*. It has small whitish-cream flowers very early in the summer and these are followed by black, juicy fruits. In the autumn the leaves turn a brilliant red. Flowering period: May-August.

the precipitation falling as snow increases with altitude, snow-patches also increase in size with altitude until the point is reached where over most of the ground more snow falls in the course of a year than melts. This is the firn-line and marks the lower limit of permanent snow, ice-fields and glaciers, although glaciers do of course flow down valleys to well below this level. Above the firn-line no vegetation can survive, except for a few isolated plants on islands of rock (nunataks) which project above the ice and in places where the rocks are too steep and the ledges too narrow for much snow to accumulate.

The lower alpine zone

BASE-POOR COMMUNITIES

As mentioned in Chapter 3, the subalpine birch woods of Fennoscandia have a ground flora that is usually dominated by dwarf shrubs, particularly bilberry *(Vaccinium myrtillus)* or crowberry. These continue above the tree-line to form the dwarf-shrub heaths which are characteristic of the lower alpine zone. On the prevailing acidic, base-poor soils and in places with only a thin snow cover or none at all, crowberry predominates, often with cowberry *(Vaccinium vitis-idaea)*, the bilberry *V. uliginosum* and alpine bearberry *(Arctostaphylos alpinus)*. The most exposed ridges often have

the trailing *Loiseleuria procumbens* and cushion-forming *Diapensia lapponica*; lichens such as *Alectoria ochroleuca* and *Cetraria nivalis* are a conspicuous feature. The few herbaceous plants include the sedge *Carex bigelowii*, the rush *Juncus trifidus* and spiked wood-rush *(Luzula spicata)*.

Where snow cover provides some protection in winter (for example along streams) shrubby willows, such as *Salix glauca* and *S. lapponum*, the dwarf birch *(Betula nana)* and juniper *(Juniperus communis)* may occur. Below and between the shrubs there is usually a well-developed carpet of mosses and lichens, notably *Cladonia alpestris*, except in places heavily grazed by reindeer. With increasing snow cover, bilberry and the purple-flowered *Phyllodoce caerulea* become dominant. Heather *(Calluna vulgaris)* is important in the southern and western mountains, while, in the far north, *Cassiope tetragona*, with its striking white, bell-shaped flowers, may be locally dominant. Herbs characteristic of the bilberry-*Phyllodoce* heaths include goldenrod *(Solidago virgaurea)*, highland cudweed *(Gnaphalium norvegicum)*, the delicate chickweed wintergreen *(Trientalis europaea)* and wavy hair-grass *(Deschampsia flexuosa)*.

With more snow cover, snow-patch vegetation develops. Dwarf shrubs are no longer able to survive and give way, usually abruptly, to grassland dominated by wavy hair-grass, often with *Carex bigelowii* and sweet vernal-grass

The dwarf shrub *Phyllodoce caerulea* is usually found on relatively base-poor rocks where snow lies throughout the winter. It has evergreen leaves and its nodding flowers grow in clusters at the end of long slender stalks. Here it is growing with the cream coloured lousewort *Pedicularis lapponica* and the rounded leaves of *Vaccinium* species. Flowering period: June-July.

The prostrate shoots of the heath *Loiseleuria procumbens* form a dense, almost cushion-like mass, covered with tiny, pink, rhododendron-like flowers. Flowering period: May-July.

Goldenrod (*Solidago virgaurea*) is a very variable plant. Mountain plants grow only 5 to 20cms tall and have fewer large yellow heads than the much taller lowland form. The cultivated goldenrods come from North America and are much taller, with many more flower heads than the European plant. Flowering period: July-September.

(*Anthoxanthum odoratum*). However, in the more oceanic west of Norway this grassland is usually dominated by mat-grass (*Nardus stricta*). Towards the centre of the snow-patch the grasses in turn give way to a prostrate mat of dwarf willow (*Salix herbacea*) and may finally be replaced by liverworts and mosses at the centre, particularly the moss *Polytrichum norvegicum*.

In Britain these plant communities are less easily recognized, partly because of the lower snowfall. As already mentioned, despite the lower latitude the tree-line is lower, not only because of the oceanicity of the climate but because of widespread deforestation and subsequent burning and grazing. The general effect of this is to convert the birch forest and the dwarf shrub communities of the lower alpine zone to managed heather moor or to grassland. As mentioned in Chapter 4 the three main types of grasslands now occurring in this zone are characterized by the dominance of different species. One is composed mainly of the grasses common bent (*Agrostis capillaris*) and sheep's-fescue (*Festuca ovina*), associated with heath bedstraw (*Galium saxatile*) and tormentil (*Potentilla erecta*); another of mat-grass and the third of the rush *Juncus squarrosus*. They occur, in this order, on soils of increasing wetness. In the English Lake District and more base-rich soils in Scotland, alpine lady's mantle (*Alchemilla alpina*) and thyme

(*Thymus praecox*) are a particular feature of the first type of *Agrostis-Festuca* grasslands and they are joined by a wide range of sedges and herbs in grassland developed over calcareous rocks. A further point of difference from Fennoscandia is the more extensive development of peaty soils and the occurrence of very extensive areas of blanket bog, even, in places, directly over limestone.

On exposed ridges in Scotland, the association of dwarf shrubs may be very similar to that in Fennoscandia, but without *Diapensia* (known from only two sites in Scotland) and nearly always with heather. Alternatively, heather may dominate but is usually associated with crowberry or bearberry (*Arctostaphylos uva-ursi*); in the east this community is rich in lichens, especially species of *Cladonia*, while in the western Highlands mosses predominate, particularly *Rhacomitrium lanuginosum*.

On more sheltered slopes the communities virtually always include heather and a variety of dwarf shrubs, particularly bilberry or, in the east, bearberry; *Phyllodoce*, though present in Scotland, is very rare. These communities extend downwards to merge into the subalpine heather moorlands. Where snow accumulates, bilberry becomes dominant but gives way towards the centre of a snow-patch to mat-grass, sometimes associated with deergrass (*Scirpus cespitosus*).

On many exposed mountain tops and ridges, flowering plants are relatively rare and vast areas are covered by hummocks of the silvery moss *Rhacomitrium lanuginosum*. Here it is seen colonizing stony ground, with only an occasional stunted conifer.

Similar communities to those found in Scotland occur in the Faeroes and Iceland, but here they are common in the lowlands as a result of widespread deforestation and overgrazing by sheep. However, grazing is less intensive than it once was: in the south and west it is now mostly restricted to the summer months, while in parts of the north it has either decreased or, as a result of depopulation, ceased completely.

The Faeroes and Iceland are geologically young volcanic islands and the basalts and tuffs of which they are formed weather easily to produce a friable, well-drained and neutral to only slightly acid soil. There is, therefore, little peat formation and the vegetation is generally richer in species.

In Iceland, the heaths usually occur on higher and more exposed sites than the grasslands. The soils are appreciably drier, have less snow cover and, being more susceptible to frost-heaving and solifluction, are characterized by prominent mounds known as *thufur*, and extensive areas of dry mud called *flag*. Crowberry, bearberry, bilberry and *Vaccinium uliginosum* are the dominant species. Heather, although often present, is rarely dominant. Also frequent in these heaths are juniper, dwarf birch, various willows and mountain avens, as well as the sedge *Kobresia myosuroides* and the mouse-ear chickweed *Cerastium alpinum*. *Loiseleuria procumbens* and *Cassiope hypnoides* become more important with increasing altitude. Low heaths with the willows *Salix phylicifolia* and *S. lanata* occur particularly in the highlands of the north-east. Vast areas, both in the lowlands and the highlands, are covered by *Rhacomitrium* heath, dominated by the silvery green carpet of the moss *R. lanuginosum*. Such heaths are favoured by the oceanic climate and are best developed on lava fields in the south and south-west. Isolated individuals of several flowering plants occur in the moss mat, for example thrift (*Armeria maritima*), *Carex bigelowii* and alpine bistort (*Polygonum viviparum*).

Grasslands occur chiefly on hillsides and in the better-drained valley bottoms. They may be dominated by the wiry *Kobresia myosuroides* or grasses such as bent (*Agrostis* species), fescues (*Festuca rubra* and *F. vivipara*) and sweet vernal-grass (*Anthoxanthum odoratum*), as well as numerous herbs such as the bedstraws *Galium sterneri* and *G. verum*, thyme, alpine bistort and the delicate *Thalictrum alpinum*. *Carex bigelowii* is particularly common in the highlands. These species-rich Icelandic grasslands are similar to the richer *Agrostis-Festuca* grasslands in Scotland, which occur mostly over limestone or calcareous schists.

In Iceland the distinction between the grasslands and the heaths is not a sharp one and there are intermediate communities characterized by mountain avens and the rush *Juncus trifidus*.

BASE-RICH COMMUNITIES

In Fennoscandia, heaths of mountain avens, covered with white flowers in early summer, are a characteristic and spectacular feature of base-rich areas in both the lower and middle alpine zones. On shallow soils and in exposed sites, mountain avens grows with the sedges *Carex rupestris*, *C. glacialis* and, more rarely, *C. nardina*. *Kobresia myosuroides* occurs on slightly deeper soils, together with dwarf shrubs, such as crowberry and the willow *Salix reticulata*, and a range of herbs which almost invariably include the purple saxifrage (*Saxifraga oppositifolia*) and moss campion (*Silene acaulis*). In northern Fennoscandia the shrubs *Cassiope tetragona* and *Rhododendron lapponicum* play an important role in these heaths, the former usually where there is some snow protection. These, combined with several colourful herbs, such as the yellow *Arnica alpina* and the pink lousewort *Pedicularis hirsuta*, make these base-rich heaths one of the most attractive of mountain plant communities during the brief northern summer. With increasing snow cover, mountain avens decreases, to be replaced first by *Salix reticulata* and the grass *Poa alpina*, and then by *Salix polaris*.

Cushions of the moss campion *(Silene acaulis)* are a common sight in the mountains, their moss-like hummocks sometimes completely covered by pink flowers. Flowering period: July-August.

Most of the flowers in the large genus *Saxifraga* are mountain plants. The purple saxifrage *(S. oppositifolia)* is commonly found in base-rich areas, where it usually forms a loose mat, covered early in the season by rosy-purple flowers. Flowering period: April-May.

The knotgrass *Polygonum viviparum* is a relatively common mountain plant. It rarely sets seed but instead reproduces by large, detachable purplish-red bulbils which are produced on the lower half of the flowering spike. The advantage of bulbils is that they are produced every year, no matter how brief the short summer flowering season. Flowering period: June-August.

In Scotland, heaths of mountain avens are very rare having been largely converted to grassland by overgrazing so that mountain avens is very largely restricted to rock ledges.

TALL HERB COMMUNITIES

In sheltered spots in the lower alpine zone where the soils are continuously moist and somewhat flushed with minerals, for example along streams and in gullies and seepage areas, there is a luxuriant and colourful vegetation of tall herbs. In Fennoscandia the monk's-hood *Aconitum septentrionale* and alpine sow-thistle *(Cicerbita alpina)*, globeflower *(Trollius europaeus)* and meadow buttercup *(Ranunculus acris)* are prominent, together with a variety of other herbs such as wood crane's-bill *(Geranium sylvaticum)* and meadowsweet *(Filipendula ulmaria)*. Many of these are also typical of the subalpine birch woods and their presence sometimes indicates a lowering of the tree-line. Similar herb-rich communities occur in Scotland and Iceland, but without monks-hood and sow-thistle, although the latter does grow in a very limited area. In Scotland tall herbs are largely restricted to ungrazed areas, especially gullies and rock ledges, where they include angelica *(Angelica sylvestris)*, globeflower and roseroot as well as typical woodland plants such as honeysuckle *(Lonicera periclymenum)* and great wood-rush *(Luzula sylvatica)*.

MIRES

Where drainage is poor and on slopes that are constantly irrigated, alpine mires may develop. These are often fringed with willow scrub in which several species may be represented, including *Salix glauca*, *S. lapponum* and *S. phylicifolia*. Similar scrub may also be found fringing lakes and streams, but, again, grazing has an adverse effect on this vegetation which then tends to become fragmented and in Scotland has almost completely disappeared. The vegetation of the mires themselves depends on the nutrient status of the water, the richest flora being in calcareous areas. Characteristic plants of calcareous mires and flushes are the yellow saxifrage *(Saxifraga aizoides)* and a distinctive sedge flora which includes *Carex atrofusca*, *C. saxatilis*, *C. microglochin* and *Kobresia simpliciuscula*, together with the rushes *Juncus biglumis*, *J. castaneus* and *J. triglumis*. These mires are usually more open than those at lower altitudes so that mosses, such as the conspicuous purplish *Scorpidium scorpioides*, *Cratoneuron commutatum* and species of *Calliergon* and *Drepanocladus*, play an important role. Less base-rich flushes usually have dense and spongy light-green cushions of the mosses *Philonotis fontana*, *Dicranella palustris* and *Pohlia wahlenbergii*, in which may be found several willowherbs, including *Epilobium alsinifolium* and *E. hornemannii*, blinks *(Montia fontana)* and the starry saxifrage *(Saxifraga stellaris)*.

Mountain lakes occur most commonly in corries which have been deeply scoured by glacial action and they are often dammed by a terminal moraine of rock debris. Since the most impermeable rocks are generally poor in nutrients, the majority of these lakes are oligotrophic, that is, they have extremely low levels of mineral nutrients and very clear water. Their beds are stony, and, as a rule, there is only a scattering of higher plants, most of which are more typical of lower altitudes. Two characteristic species are the quillworts *Isoetes lacustris* and *I. echinospora* which in Britain are often associated at lower altitudes with the water lobelia *(Lobelia dortmanna)*.

The middle alpine zone

The boundary between the lower and middle alpine zones is generally recognized by a change from dwarf-shrub heath to grass-heath; the shrubby willows, juniper and dwarf heaths disappear and, particularly important, so also does the bilberry. This change is, however, not always very pronounced especially in areas where the soil is base-rich and bilberry is already scarce or absent, as is the case in much of central and southern Iceland and in parts of northern Fennoscandia. Furthermore, some shrubs, such as crowberry, continue far up into this zone and in northern Fennoscandia mountain avens and *Cassiope tetragona* form very important heaths here, but with fewer other species and on a wider range of soils than in the lower alpine zone.

The term grass-heath is rather misleading as three of the most important plants are not grasses, these being the rush *Juncus trifidus*, the wood-rush *Luzula arcuata* and the sedge *Carex bigelowii*. Of the grasses, sheep's-fescue and the related *Festuca vivipara* are the commonest. These grass-heaths, rich in lichens, are best developed on level or sloping areas which tend to be blown fairly free of snow. They seldom form a continuous cover and this is especially so on ridges and summit plateaux.

In western Norway and Britain summit heaths of *Rhacomitrium lanuginosum* are common, usually on ground with a slight snow cover. They are similar to the conspicuous *Rhacomitrium* heaths of Iceland. Wind erosion is a constant feature of the Scottish sites and the vegetation is usually a mosaic of moss, fescue grassland and open, stony fell-field, with only isolated individuals of *Juncus trifidus*, fescue, thyme, alpine lady's-mantle and *Minuartia sedoides*. Although there is plenty of evidence of stabilization and colonization it seems that erosion may be increasing.

In Fennoscandia, sites with a moderate snow cover are characterized by the shrubs *Phyllodoce caerulea* and the delicate mossy *Cassiope hypnoides*. With longer but not too persistent snow-lie the grasses *Deschampsia caespitosa* or the closely related viviparous *D. alpina* and mat-grass may become dominant. This is true also in Scotland and Iceland.

Left: The yellow saxifrage *(Saxifraga aizoides)* is especially characteristic of base-rich mires, flushes and streamsides. The yellow petals are often spotted with red and so may look orange. Flowering period: June-August.

Below: The yellow violet *Viola biflora* grows in damp and shady places, mainly in the mountains of Fennoscandia. Unlike other violets its lateral petals point upwards and it has kidney-shaped leaves. Flowering period: June-July.

Mountain sorrel *(Oxyria digyna)* is a dock-like plant, easily recognized by its kidney-shaped leaves. It grows in damp, rocky places and is often found in very late snow-patches where it may be uncovered for only a few weeks of the year. Flowering period: July-August.

As in the lower alpine zone, herb-slopes may occur in favourable flushed sites, often facing south and below cliffs or lingering snow-patches. They support an attractive and rich collection of plants such as *Thalictrum alpinum*, the speedwell *Veronica alpina*, *Potentilla crantzii*, *Sibbaldia procumbens*, alpine lady's-mantle and other species of *Alchemilla*, the grass *Phleum alpinum* and various dandelions *(Taraxacum* species). The Fennoscandian herb-slopes also include the delicate yellow-flowered *Viola biflora*.

In Scotland, the prevalence of these and many other 'alpines' on rock ledges and in gullies is due not only to the absence of grazing animals but to the fact that frequent rock falls and the detachment of large, unstable cushions of vegetation constantly create open habitats.

Snow-patches occupy a larger area than in the lower alpine zone but their vegetation is essentially the same. Dwarf willow is again the usual dominant species, often with the dwarf cudweed *(Gnaphalium supinum)* and, in Fennoscandia and Iceland, *Cassiope hypnoides*. Very late snow-patches are likely to have mountain sorrel *(Oxyria digyna)* and the sedge *Carex lachenalii*, while the centre may be occupied only by liverworts, especially species of *Gymnomitrium* and *Anthelia*, the latter forming bluish-white cushions, and mosses, notably *Polytrichum norvegicum* and *Dicranum*

starkei. On calcareous soils the sorrel may be joined by purple saxifrage, the saxifrage *Saxifraga rivularis*, the mouse-ear chickweed *Cerastium cerastoides*, alpine rock-cress *(Arabis alpina)* and, in open mossy sites, the diminutive grass *Phippsia algida*.

The upper alpine zone

Conditions in the upper alpine zone are very severe. Temperatures never rise more than a few degrees above freezing; frosts, and therefore solifluction, may occur throughout the summer; snow is very late melting and gales are frequent. Not surprisingly, therefore, the plant cover is sparse. The commonest plants are mosses, liverworts and lichens, and flowering plants usually occur only as isolated individuals. Large areas of frost-shattered debris are frequent, particularly on plateaux, and these are almost devoid of flowering plants. The most sheltered sites are usually snow-patches and one of the commonest plants in the lower part of this zone is the dwarf willow. Other very characteristic species are the wood-rush *Luzula arcuata*, the cress *Cardamine bellidifolia*, the clubmoss *Lycopodium selago* and the grasses *Deschampsia alpina*, and *Poa arctica* and, especially, *Poa flexuosa*. The most conspicuous plant of this zone in Fennoscandia is the white- or lilac-flowered buttercup *Ranunculus glacialis*, which grows at a higher altitude than any other flowering plant in north-west Europe: 2055m on Kebnekaise in northern Sweden. Mosses and lichens usually continue above the last flowering plants right up to the firn line.

Iceland and the Faeroes

It is particularly difficult to apply the altitudinal zones to Iceland. This is not only because of the extensive deforestation, or the rarity, in some areas, of the important indicator species bilberry, but because there are very many habitats at low altitudes which are suitable for mountain plants. As mentioned above, the rocks weather readily, producing material which is very susceptible to erosion by physical processes and by overgrazing. Melt-water rivers flowing down from the extensive ice-caps carry enormous amounts of sand, gravel and volcanic ash, building up vast out-wash areas with intricate and ever-changing patterns of channels. These areas provide a ready source of material which is picked up and transported often considerable distances by the frequent gales. In fact, most of the Icelandic soils are of wind-borne origin. A further source of wind-borne material is soil exposed by overgrazing and the disruption of the plant cover by sheep rubbing and scraping hollows. These factors, combined with the high permeability of the soil and often of the underlying rock also, the low rainfall (especially in the north-east) and the disruptive effects of solifluction and frost-heaving, mean that much of the land is at any one moment either being actively eroded or suffering fresh deposition. The result is a country which, especially in the uplands, is largely devoid of vegetation; indeed it has been estimated that only a fifth of Iceland has plant cover.

The freshly eroded or deposited surfaces are desert-like and support scattered individuals of only a few species. The removal of sand and soil leaves a surface layer of gravel. Vast areas, known as *sandar* or *melar*, are in this state. They are characterized by several species normally associated with the middle or even upper alpine zone, including some of the hardiest of arctic plants. These include moss campion, the mouse-ear chickweed *Cerastium alpinum*, purple saxifrage, dwarf willow, the grass *Poa glauca* and the cress *Cardaminopsis petraea*. Areas of sand and sand-dunes provide a habitat for coastal species such as lyme-grass (*Leymus arenarius*), sea campion (*Silene vulgaris* subsp. *maritima*), thrift (*Armeria maritima*) and the northern sea-shore sedge *Carex maritima*. There are, in addition, considerable areas in the lowlands of unstable moraine, outwash fans and river gravel- and sand-flats. These support many of the *melar* species and, where the material is more

stable, the striking purple-flowered willowherb *Epilobium latifolium*. This plant often dominates considerable areas both in the lowlands and the highlands and, when flowering, provides the naturalist with one of the most beautiful sights in Iceland. It is a circumpolar species, but restricted in north-west Europe to Iceland.

By contrast, despite their similar geology, the Faeroes have a relatively continuous plant cover in the lowlands. This is probably because they have high rainfall and no glaciers. The species to be found in the fell-field of the higher mountains, above 600m, are similar to those in Iceland and include many of the *melar* species together with the buttercup *Ranunculus glacialis* and the saxifrages *Saxifraga nivalis* and *S. rosacea*.

Mountain plants below the tree-line

The tree-line is not necessarily the natural lower limit for mountain plants and many occur well below it in sites which are not heavily shaded and where there is little competition from other species. Such sites may be rocky bluffs or treeless outcrops of ultrabasic rocks, such as serpentine, or gravel- and sand-banks along forest streams and rivers. Mountain avens, for example, has a number of riverside sites in the coniferous forests of southern Norway. Very characteristic of such communities are several plants of wet flushes, such as yellow saxifrage.

In the north and west, where the tree-line is lower, many mountain plants not surprisingly reach their lowest altitude, sometimes descending to sea-level. In Scotland, for example, a number of species found no lower than 300–460m in the east may be found at sea-level in the north-west. One striking example is the formation of dune-heath with bearberry, mountain crowberry and mountain avens on the north coast of Sutherland.

There are a number of well known areas in north-west Europe where mountain plants can be found at low altitudes, some of the species being far removed from their nearest mountain localities. The best known of these are the Burren area of Co Clare in western Ireland and the Swedish islands of Öland and Gotland in the Baltic Sea, all characterized by having large areas of exposed limestone. It is now accepted that these limestone areas were not entirely tree-covered during the Post-glacial period and this allowed the relict populations of mountain plants to survive. A few species occur in both areas, for example shrubby cinquefoil (*Potentilla fruticosa*), a northern species which is montane in southern Europe. On Öland, the flora includes the blue-flowered *Globularia vulgaris*, a southern montane species, the alpine catchfly (*Lychnis alpina*) of the Alps and northern Europe, and the circumpolar *Androsace septentrionalis*, although this is not really a montane species. The Burren

Left: The plant that occurs at the highest altitudes in the mountains of our region is the white- or lilac-flowered buttercup *Ranunculus glacialis*. It has fleshy leaves and usually grows in areas irrigated by melt-water. It is able to grow even when the temperature is below freezing point. Flowering period: June-August.

On these open gravelly deposits of volcanic material in Iceland are hummocks of white-flowered sea campion (*Silene vulgaris* subsp. *maritima*) and more extensive reddish patches of the knotgrass *Polygonum viviparum*. Flowering period: May-August.

In our region, the willowherb *Epilobium latifolium* is confined to Iceland, where with its large magenta flowers it is a particularly attractive feature of river gravels and other open stony areas. Flowering period: July-August.

flora includes the bearberry, mountain avens and the spring gentian, a species of the southern and central European mountains, only found elsewhere in north-west Europe in the Pennines of northern England. Also in the Burren are southern lowland species such as the maidenhair fern (*Adiantum capillus-veneris*) and the dense-flowered orchid (*Neotinea intacta*); these occur here not, like the mountain plants, because of the cool maritime summers, but because of the mildness of the winters.

The adaptations of mountain plants

To be able to grow in mountain environments plants must possess a variety of adaptations. They must, for example, be able to germinate, grow and photosynthesize efficiently at lower temperatures than plants at lower altitudes. The mountain sorrel and the buttercup *Ranunculus glacialis*, for example, can photosynthesize at temperatures as low as −6°C. In some cases it has been shown that such adaptations characterize montane populations of species which also occur at lower altitudes. Presumably many plants are also

adapted to the extreme conditions on exposed ridges and crests where they are subject to physical damage and very low temperatures in the winter and drought conditions which often prevail, particularly in the more continental areas, in early spring and occasionally late summer.

Plants use a variety of devices to counter the shortness of the growing season, which, in the case of plants in late snow-patches, may only allow about a month for flowering and the development of ripe seed. Indeed, one of the characteristic features of mountain plants is the speed with which they flower after, and sometimes even before, the snow has melted. This is achieved by the development of the flower buds the previous summer so that they are ready to open as soon as conditions are favourable. The harsh environment also reduces the number and variety of insects which can visit and pollinate the flowers; many of the plants which do produce seed are therefore automatically self-pollinated, the anthers shedding their pollen over the stigmas often before the flowers have opened. Seed development in some plants such as the yellow-flowered arctic poppy *Papaver radicatum*, which grows in Iceland, the Faeroes and Fennoscandia, is helped by large bowl-shaped flowers which act as parabolic reflectors for the sun's rays, warming the central ovary containing the developing ovules and seeds.

Saxifraga cernua usually has a single white flower at the end of its flowering stem, but apparently never produces seed. Instead it regenerates by means of small red bulbils which drop off the flowering stem and become new plants. Flowering period: July.

The poppy *Papaver radicatum* is one of four similar species found in the far north of Europe. All have yellow or white petals, but details of the fruiting capsule and leaves are different. They are usually found in open, rather stony ground. Flowering period: July.

The vast majority of mountain plants are perennials and many are capable of vegetative propagation by means of runners and rhizomes. This enables them to survive for long periods without relying on seed production. In some species the flowers are replaced by vegetative structures which become detached and allow far wider dispersal than is possible by runners or rhizomes. This is the case in the viviparous grasses *Deschampsia alpina* and *Festuca vivipara*, in which the flowers are replaced by small plantlets. In other grasses, such as *Poa alpina*, some individuals are viviparous and some produce seeds. In the alpine bistort the upper flowers are normal while the lower ones are replaced by small compact bulbils, small buds that develop into separate plants. Bulbils are also a feature of *Saxifraga cernua* although here they are produced in the axils of the leaves. The saxifrage apparently never produces seed and the bistort only rarely.

In some species which are annuals at low altitudes, the plants growing at high altitudes may not be able to flower in their first season and so behave as biennials or short-lived perennials. However, there are a few annual mountain plants which can pass through their entire life-cycle during the brief summer. These include the striking, deep blue-flowered *Gentiana nivalis* and the diminutive *Koenigia islandica*, a member of the dock family.

Distribution and history

It will already be only too evident that the floras of the different mountain areas in our region are by no means the same. In part this is due to the location and degree of isolation of the mountains. In the British Isles the mountains are isolated and limited in area. This, together with their southerly position, relatively low altitude and also, possibly, the effects of heavy grazing, gives an impoverished mountain flora. Iceland, though even more isolated and having a smaller flora overall, is nevertheless that much nearer the Arctic and consequently has a rather richer mountain flora. A high proportion of its native species occur also in the Fennoscandian mountains which have by far the richest mountain flora in north-west Europe, though still much less varied than that of the Alps.

Fossil remains of many of the present-day Fennoscandian mountain plants, dating from the Late-glacial and early Post-glacial periods, have been found in the lowlands as far south as Germany. These indicate that as the ice receded northwards, the ground was progressively colonized by a wide range of predominantly mountain plants. It is generally assumed that they were subsequently able to colonize the Fennoscandian mountains at or even before the time when the main Fennoscandian ice-sheets finally disappeared. A contrary view is that in the early Post-glacial period forests advanced northwards over the lowlands so rapidly that they eliminated most of these potential invaders. This implies that the Fennoscandian mountains were colonized from the north-east rather than the south. Certainly this north-eastern route from arctic Russia into northern Norway has played an important role in plant migration, judging by the number of arctic species in Fennoscandia which are absent from the mountains of central Europe.

However, the flora of any one area is a mixture of species with differing histories and migrations. Some species are very widespread, occurring in virtually all the main mountain areas in north-west Europe as well as in the mountains of southern and central Europe and in the Arctic. Such plants, of which the purple saxifrage and the mountain sorrel are good examples, are said to have an arctic-montane, or arctic-alpine, distribution. Most of the mountain plants in our region have similar distributions but are missing in particular areas. The willow *Salix reticulata*, for example, although it has a widespread arctic-montane distribution is curiously absent from Iceland and Greenland. On the other hand, *Salix polaris* is essentially an arctic species; it occurs in Fennoscandia but is absent from the eastern Canadian Arctic to Iceland. The dwarf willow, the commonest mountain willow, has what is called an amphi-Atlantic distribution, spanning both sides of the Atlantic: it extends westwards into

Canada and eastwards to just beyond the Urals. This is a well-defined type of distribution which is shared by *Juncus trifidus*.

One remarkable distribution within the region is that of the grass *Alopecurus alpinus*. This is a circumpolar high-arctic species which is absent from Iceland and Fennoscandia, yet occurs in isolated places in the mountains of Scotland and northern England. A few of the mountain plants are southern species, having a European distribution centred on the Alps. The spring gentian of northern England and western Ireland has already been mentioned. Another example is *Minuartia sedoides*, an inconspicuous cushion-forming plant endemic to Europe with an isolated northern occurrence in the Scottish mountains. The only species entirely restricted to the mountains of the British Isles, Iceland and Fennoscandia, is the sandwort *Arenaria norvegica*.

On a smaller scale, there are puzzling localized distributions which may either be interpreted as relict populations of a once wider distribution following the retreat of the ice, or as populations which have survived at or near their present sites through the vicissitudes of the last and possibly earlier glaciations. This latter theory of glacial survival has been widely used to explain why so many mountain plants are restricted to particular areas, for example, Teesdale in northern England, Dovrefjell and other mountain areas in south Norway and a larger area in both Norway and Sweden north of the Arctic Circle. Certainly, in the case of Teesdale, we know that many of the rare species were widely distributed in Britain during the Late-glacial period.

There are still many botanists who believe that some Fennoscandian plants, including most of the uni- and bicentric species, probably survived the last glaciation on nearby coastal mountains projecting through the ice and that they subsequently migrated inland. Others think that their present distributions can be explained by the combination in the two areas of a relatively dry continental climate and the prevalence of base-rich habitats, taking into account also the reduction in the area available to mountain plants during the warmest phase of the Post-glacial period.

Finally, mention must be made of two species in the otherwise unremarkable mountain flora of Ireland. These are the saxifrages *Saxifraga spathularis* and *S. hirsuta*. The former has a fairly wide distribution in Ireland, but the latter is now restricted to the south-west. Both occur nowhere else in north-west Europe, but have their main area of distribution in the northern part of the Iberian peninsula. Such puzzles are part of the fascination of studying plant distributions, which reflect past migrations, soil and climatic preferences, and the imponderable effects of chance.

7
Rivers, lakes and streams

North-west Europe is well watered. The ice sheets of the glacial periods gouged out long, deep lakes from the mountains and left behind widespread moraines, in the hollows of which water accumulated to give shallow pools and swamps. The high rainfall, well distributed through the year, ensures a regular supply of water to the many rivers, and the very wide range of rock types of all geological ages adds further variety. Man has subtracted from this initial richness by drainage and pollution, but has added reservoirs, gravel pits, canals and ditches for land reclamation and irrigation.

Comparatively few plants live in water. Why should this be, and how does water differ from land as a plant habitat? First, water is much less transparent than air. Even in the clearest water of the open oceans, light only penetrates to a depth of about 50m, and in fresh waters the zone in which there is enough light for plant growth is almost always much less because of suspended clay, organic matter, phytoplankton and the yellowish materials dissolved from humus in the soil. Second, as well as light, plants require gases for photosynthesis and respiration. Gases diffuse about ten thousand times more slowly in water than in air, so waterlogged soils often lack oxygen completely, as diffusion is too slow to replace consumption by micro-organisms. In the resulting anaerobic conditions, foul-smelling, poisonous sulphides and amines may be formed. However, the roots and rhizomes of most water plants are permeated by a system of air canals, which are continuations of similar canals in the rest of the plant. Through these, oxygen can diffuse into the underground parts. A bonus of the system is that it gives buoyancy to the plant, supporting it in an upright position without the need for more strengthening tissue than is necessary to resist the pull of waves and water currents.

Water plants obtain their carbon for photosynthesis from dissolved carbon dioxide or bicarbonate ions. Their leaves are usually either very thin and membranous, or delicate and

The common reed (*Phragmites australis*) is perhaps the most widespread of all lake-fringing plants. It can grow in water to a depth of around 60cm, and its dead remains slowly build up until they reach the water surface. The leaves pivot around the stem, aligning themselves downwind. Flowering period: August–September.

hair-like. This means that gases only have to diffuse short distances from the water to the fixation sites in the plant cells. The other substances that a plant needs can be obtained either from the soil, through the roots, or from the water, through the leaves.

Few plants seem to have managed anything but an uneasy compromise with the problems of flowering in water. Cross-pollination requires an agent to transfer the pollen, and water is unsuitable for this because pollen grains burst when immersed in fresh water. This does not happen in sea water, so a few marine plants, such as eelgrass (Zostera species), have water-dispersed pollen. Most water plants, however, produce their flowers above the surface. Many of them evade the issue altogether and flower only occasionally, reproducing vegetatively by fragments or buds. The Canadian waterweed (Elodea canadensis), introduced to Britain in 1842, produces seeds only very rarely and seems to have spread entirely vegetatively.

Still-water habitats: lakes and ponds

North-west Europe is quite rich in lakes. Many, as already mentioned, were produced by glacial deepening of valleys or damming by moraines. Other, coastal, lakes have their origins in land/sea-level changes. A third kind of lake is the oxbow or abandoned meander, produced by a change in the course of a river; such lakes are usually short-lived. The majority of still waters in the lowland, heavily populated areas of Europe are largely artificial.

Lakes may be divided into three classes, according to their nutritive content. Dystrophic lakes are very poor in lime and other nutrients, and, partly as a consequence of this, contain peaty material both on the bottom and in solution. There is virtually no biological activity during the summer. Oligotrophic lakes are slightly richer in nutrients, and, because of this, biological activity occurs during the summer but is insufficient to remove all the oxygen from the deeper water. Such lakes, therefore, remain oxygenated right to the bottom throughout the year. Eutrophic lakes are much richer and the flush of plant growth during the summer months is enough to remove most of the oxygen from the deeper layers. Clearly there are intermediates and man, by adding nutrients in sewage effluent or as fertilizer running off treated crops, can turn an oligotrophic lake into a eutrophic one.

Dystrophic lakes and pools occur mainly in the cool and wet, highly oceanic parts of north-west Europe. They are usually set in peatland areas and surrounded by vegetation dominated by the bog moss Sphagnum (see Chapter 8). The brown peaty water of the pools allows plant growth only in the shallows, where the sparse vegetation includes plants of bog pools such as the bogbean (Menyanthes trifoliata), the

insectivorous bladderworts (Utricularia species) and the pondweed Potamogeton polygonifolius.

The plant life of an oligotrophic lake depends greatly on the lake's size and depth. Only the shallow edges of deep lakes can be colonized by plants, and if the lake is large, this marginal zone is liable to be battered by waves. Large, deep oligotrophic lakes are frequent in north-west Britain and in Fennoscandia. For instance, about 10 per cent of Finland is covered by them. Many of the plants of these lakes have rosettes of basal leaves, but although they share this growth form they are not otherwise related. The most decorative is water lobelia (Lobelia dortmanna), whose delicate, pale lilac flowers rise above the water on long stalks in late summer.

Lobelia is only really frequent in the more oceanic parts of north-west Europe; the commoner shoreweed (Littorella uniflora) has a much wider range. Its creeping runners allow it to form extensive mats but it only flowers when it is left exposed by low water levels. Also widespread, extending, like shoreweed, even to Iceland, are the two species of quillwort (Isoetes lacustris and I. echinospora), which form dark green rosettes of quill-like leaves. Quillwort is found down to at least 10m in clear waters and often covers large areas like a lawn. Another plant with the same growth form and habitat, although more northerly in distribution, is awlwort (Subularia aquatica), a tiny plant which usually

Left: Eutrophic lakes are usually set in the lowlands, often in areas of soft rocks. The nutrient content of the water is high and the vegetation both in and around the lake is rich in species.

Below: Oligotrophic lakes are usually set in mountainous areas where the rocks are hard and base-poor. Here the movement of waves keeps the shore free of plants, though there is probably a carpet of vegetation below water level.

produces its yellow flowers when exposed by low water levels. It can also produce underwater flowers which do not open but are self-fertilized in the bud. The rosette growth form shared by these species is resistant to wave turbulence; in more sheltered sites taller plants can grow and overshadow the rosette plants. These taller plants include the filamentous-leaved rush *Juncus bulbosus* var. *fluitans* and *Scirpus fluitans*, both found particularly in the most nutrient-poor, almost dystrophic waters, often with small forms of the white water-lily *(Nymphaea alba)*. In slightly richer waters throughout north-west Europe except in the extreme north, large pondweed species such as *Potamogeton perfoliatus*, *P. obtusifolius* and *P. praelongus* often occupy the more sheltered sites, their stems reaching 5m or more in length. The growth of the large pondweeds is favoured by the clarity of many oligotrophic lakes where the low nutrient content of the water does not allow large populations of phytoplankton to develop; in more eutrophic lakes phytoplankton can shade out submerged plants.

At the stony edges of oligotrophic lakes, shoreweed is often abundant and may be joined by the minute, almost moss-like mats of *Elatine hexandra* or *E. hydropiper*, with the small creeping buttercup *Ranunculus reptans* in Fennoscandia and Iceland or pillwort *(Pilularia globulifera)* in the west. Most of these species depend upon a fall in water

Ranunculus peltatus is one of many white-flowered water crowfoots. It usually has two types of leaves. Those below the surface are finely divided while the floating ones are kidney-shaped or semi-circular. The species with floating leaves are usually those found in still waters such as ponds and ditches. Flowering period: May-August.

level for flowering, and are therefore most at home in the smaller lakes where water levels are more likely to fluctuate.

Because of their higher nutrient content, eutrophic lakes usually contain many more species and individual plants than oligotrophic lakes. Lakes of this kind are most frequent in the lowlands of north-west Europe. Fine examples of eutrophic lake vegetation are found in the Netherlands, Belgium and eastern England, although some of the best vegetation is now to be found in drainage ditches rather than in natural lakes and pools. Pondweeds are often the most abundant submerged plants of these sites, accompanied by Canadian waterweed and by two species of water-milfoil, *Myriophyllum spicatum* and *M. verticillatum*. Some of the white-flowered water buttercups, such as *Ranunculus circinatus* and *R. peltatus*, are also characteristic. Like many other water plants, water buttercups and pondweeds are often difficult to identify because they are very variable in size and form. For example, the size of the leaves can vary with the amount of nutrients in the water; their shape can change with depth; and plants growing in shallow water may produce leaves which float on the surface as well as submerged leaves, the two kinds sometimes looking very different.

Other plants confined to still waters are those which are unattached to the substrate, the lake or pond bed. The most familiar of these are the duckweeds (*Lemna* species), minute, disc-like plants which are undifferentiated into stems and leaves and which multiply rapidly by budding. They float freely on the water, moving about with wind and current, and sometimes form a continuous carpet covering the whole surface. Their flowers are minute, and in north-west Europe are formed only in hot summers. Other, larger, but still free-floating plants are the water ferns, *Salvinia* and the introduced *Azolla*, the larger and more decorative frogbit (*Hydrocharis morsus-ranae*) and the water-soldier (*Stratiotes aloides*). The last produces large rosettes of leaves looking like pineapple tops; these sink to the bottom during the winter and float up again the next spring, apparently because of changes in the amount of lime encrusting the leaves. The water ferns, frogbit and water-soldier are absent from the cooler and more Atlantic parts of north-west Europe. Frogbit, for instance, extends northwards only to England and Wales and to southern Sweden, while *Azolla* and *Salvinia* are even more restricted. Most of these plants are common in the Dutch and Belgium lowlands and in the backwaters of the Rhine in southern Germany. At the limits of their ranges they flower only rarely and hardly ever produce spores or seeds; frogbit and water-soldier reproduce almost entirely by producing new rosettes on the ends of short stolons.

Nearer the lake edges grow those species which are rooted

In lowland areas drainage ditches are often the only remaining refuges for aquatic plants. Here the white water lily *(Nymphaea alba)* covers part of the open water with its broad leaves while the common reed *(Phragmites australis)* spreads from the shallower waters at the sides. Flowering period: July-August.

Right: Plants which float freely and are not rooted are usually confined to ponds or ditches. Frog bit *(Hydrocharis morsus-ranae)* has white flowers with three petals, and rounded, kidney-shaped floating leaves. The duckweed *Lemna minor,* which surrounds it here, is little more than a flat, floating mass of green cells, with a single root. *Lemna* flowers consist only of a minute ovary or stamen. Flowering period: June-August.

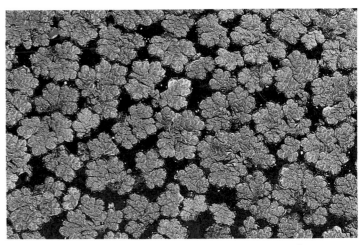

Azolla filiculoides is a free-floating water fern from North America which has spread through the warmer parts of the region. The leaves have two divisions, or lobes. The upper lobes, only about 1mm across, float on the surface and have cavities containing a blue-green alga. In winter they change colour from green to pinkish red. The lower lobes are submerged and bear the reproductive structures.

The water soldier *(Stratiotes aloides)* grows underwater for part of the year but rises to the surface when it flowers. At this time, the plants resemble pineapple tops, with white flowers like those of the frog bit. It is becoming less common as a result of improved drainage. Flowering period: June-August.

in the lake bottom but produce floating leaves. The most familiar of these are the water-lilies, yellow *(Nuphar lutea)* and white *(Nymphaea alba* and *N. candida).* The first two are widespread but *N. candida* is absent from the more Atlantic parts of the region. *Nuphar* has both submerged and floating leaves, growing from a massive horizontal rhizome which is firmly rooted in the mud surface. The leaves appear in the spring and die down in the autumn and the yellow flowers, followed by the bottle-shaped fruits, are produced in high summer. The white water-lilies have only floating leaves but their flowers rest on the water surface instead of being held above it. The water-lilies do not seem to be part of any very obvious plant community; their leaves cast a dense shade which excludes other species below them. Probably the natural distribution of the species has been obscured by introductions. The yellow water-lily also occurs in slow-flowing lowland rivers, sometimes then having only submerged leaves. Other species common to river backwaters as well as lakes are the fringed water-lily *(Nymphoides peltatus)*, only distantly related to the true water-lilies, and the water chestnut *(Trapa natans)*. The distinctive large, spiny fruits of the water chestnut are often found as subfossil remains in lake muds, and show that in the past the species grew further north in Europe than it does today. Fossil fruits are common in the Netherlands for example, and in southern Sweden they have been found as far north as Uppsala; the plant is now extinct in both countries. Dating of the mud layers in which the fossil fruits are found shows that the water chestnut occurred in these northernmost localities during the warmest part of the Post-glacial period and its retreat is believed to be due to the subsequent climatic deterioration. Within its present range it has also declined. As rivers are more controlled and embanked, they are prevented from meandering and so oxbow lakes, its preferred habitat, are no longer formed.

The edges of lakes are often occupied by reed swamp. The plants of this type of vegetation are tall monocotyledons with roots and perennial rhizomes below the water and tall, usually annual, aerial shoots. The best known is the common reed *(Phragmites australis)*. Many of the extensive reed beds of lowland Europe have disappeared as a result of drainage but some remain, supporting a community of interesting and unusual birds such as bearded tits *(Panurus biarmicus)* and bitterns *(Botaurus stellaris* and *Ixobrychus minutus)*, and exploited by local people for thatching material. The tall annual stems of another reed-swamp plant, the common clubrush *(Scirpus lacustris)*, are also harvested and used for weaving into mats and baskets. It is a common species of reed swamps and of the edges of slow rivers, growing in up to 2m of water. Other species of this habitat are the bulrushes *Typha latifolia* and *T. angustifolia. Typha latifolia* is often

The sweet-flag *(Acorus calamus)* is a relative of the wild arum, but has a flowering spike (the spadix) densely covered by small yellowish flowers without the usual surrounding pale petal-like spathe. The wrinkles on the scented leaves are particularly characteristic of this plant. Flowering period: May-July.

Below: At the edges of lakes and slow-flowing rivers there is often a zone of tall, reed-like plants. One of these is the bulrush *(Typha latifolia)*. The thick lower part of the spike, formed of tightly packed female flowers, has numerous tiny fruits, each surrounded by hairs which allow it to be dispersed by wind. Flowering period: June-July.

The yellow water-lily *(Nuphar lutea)* is widespread in still waters or slowly-flowing rivers. Unlike the white water-lily *(Nymphaea alba)* it usually has large, thin, translucent, submerged leaves as well as the more familiar floating ones. The flowers grow up above the water surface and are replaced by a large, flask-shaped fruit. Flowering period: June-August.

common around small ponds. Finally, mention should be made of the bur-reed *Sparganium erectum,* which is often found fringing lakes and ponds, and is also very common at the edges of slower lowland rivers. It produces its branched spikes of spherical fruiting heads in late summer.

It is often difficult to explain why one reed-swamp species and not another occurs in a particular place. Both the common reed and the bulrushes have very light, wind-dispersed seeds which can easily reach new habitats. Once there, they can quickly spread vegetatively and exclude other species. It is possible, in fact, that the dominance of a particular reed-swamp species in a particular site is largely a matter of chance.

THE SUCCESSION OF VEGETATION

The vegetation of lakes is often arranged in approximately concentric zones, with submerged plants occupying the deepest water farthest from the shore, floating-leaved plants in shallower water, and finally reed swamp closest to the shore. Do these zones eventually replace one another? The accumulation of dead plant material could raise the level of the lake bottom allowing, for instance, water-lilies to spread into areas previously occupied by pondweeds, and reed swamp to spread over former water-lily areas. This succession, called a hydrosere, may finish with the conversion of open water into dry land, which could eventually be colonized by woodland.

Probably the most convincing evidence that succession of this kind actually takes place comes from borings which show that deep beneath some woodlands lie lake deposits, overlain by reed-swamp peats and then by peat containing wood of trees of wet ground, such as alder *(Alnus glutinosa)* and willows *(Salix* species). Other valuable evidence comes from the periodic mapping of sites. Such data show that in nutrient-rich lakes succession can and does proceed quite rapidly, with open water being replaced by reed swamp at rates of up to 1m each year. In some of the very nutrient-poor lochs of Scotland, however, no difference can be detected between photographs taken more than fifty years apart. Here, then, succession must be extremely slow. Presumably the situation is similar in other upland areas of north-west Europe.

Flowing water habitats: rivers and streams

In contrast to still waters, flowing waters, particularly if they are subject to large floods, pose problems of anchorage to the plant. In the upper reaches of rivers, the slope is usually steep and the flow is therefore fast. The fast-flowing waters remove all but the largest stones and leave little opportunity for plants to grow. Mosses and liverworts (bryophytes)

dominate this type of stream. They form low tussocks and mats which are firmly attached to the rocks and offer little resistance to the flowing water. They are also very tolerant of desiccation, and can stay alive for a long time if the stream dries up, reviving quickly when flow restarts. Bryophytes are very particular about the type of rock on which they grow, and so streams running over different kinds of rock usually carry different bryophyte communities. Upland streams on hard rocks often have the more varied flora, particularly if the rocks are rich in mineral nutrients. Lowland streams usually flow more slowly and are often shaded or heavily overgrown with higher plants so that bryophytes are excluded.

Further from the stream's source the slope decreases and the rate of flow slackens. The stream bed is still coarse-grained but is now gravelly or sandy instead of rocky. The plants growing in this part of the river are often large, totally submerged and have filamentous leaves. Many species of water buttercup are often found here, forming long, waving masses up to 2 or 3m long. *Ranunculus fluitans* is the species most frequently found in relatively nutrient-poor rivers, often accompanied by another species of water milfoil,

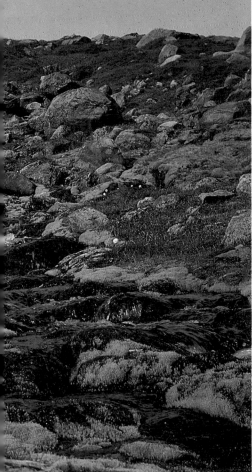

Above left: Most water crowfoots characteristic of flowing water, such as *Ranunculus fluitans,* do not generally have floating leaves; their finely divided submerged leaves offer little resistance to the current. Only the flowers appear above the surface. Flowering period: June–August.

Left: In fast-flowing mountain streams, mosses and liverworts are usually the dominant plants and cover the rocks in and beside the water.

Right: Hemlock water-dropwort *(Oenanthe crocata)* is found only in the extreme west of the region, where it grows in fens and at stream or riversides. It looks not unlike celery but is very poisonous. Flowering period: June–July.

Myriophyllum alterniflorum. Bryophytes occupy the surface of any rocks exposed in the river bed, and also grow on the partially submerged roots of riverside trees. On seasonally exposed rocks or shingle at the edge of the river, a distinct group of plants occurs, among which the extremely poisonous hemlock water-dropwort *(Oenanthe crocata)* is prominent, often accompanied by introduced North American monkey flowers *(Mimulus* species).

Rivers cannot be classified in the same way as lakes; factors such as flow rate and nutrient content vary too much with time, and the rivers form a continuous series from nutrient-poor to nutrient-rich. They are also usually well oxygenated because of their flow. Some of the most nutrient-rich rivers are those on the limestones of southern England and northern France. These rise from springs fed from deep within the permeable chalk. Flow varies little from season to season and the temperature remains remarkably constant. The water, filtered through the chalk, is extremely clear and highly alkaline. These rivers carry dense swards of submerged vegetation, in which water buttercups, especially *Ranunculus penicillatus* var. *calcareus*, are usually dominant, together with species of water starwort *(Callitriche)*, and various aquatic umbellifers, such as *Berula erecta, Apium nodiflorum* and species of *Oenanthe*.

Most of these chalk streams are no longer in their natural state. They have been diverted by weirs to drive mills or to fill watercress *(Nasturtium officinale)* beds and fish ponds, and are now used for high quality trout fishing. The masses of vegetation shelter huge populations of invertebrate animals upon which the trout feed and grow fat, while the clarity of the water makes approach very difficult, providing both a challenge and a possible large reward for the angler. The weeds grow so vigorously that by midsummer they can obstruct the flow of the river and they are therefore cut at least once a year to prevent flooding. Cutting stimulates further growth and by the autumn there may once again be enough weed to require cutting before the winter floods. The whole chalk stream system, in fact, is man-made and man-maintained. Natural rivers would flow through dense alder and willow woodland, the shade preventing the growth of water plants and the tree roots stabilizing the banks and restricting the river to a deep, narrow channel.

The lower reaches of rivers flow even more slowly; often the river meanders gently through a broad flood plain, with still backwaters and oxbows giving a rich range of aquatic habitats. Sadly, the lower reaches of most European rivers now carry such a load of pollutants that few contain many plants, while flood protection works have often straightened the course and eliminated the backwaters. The slow flow allows fine particles to settle and the bottom is usually muddy or silty. It also allows algae to multiply, considerably

The yellow iris *(Iris pseudacorus)* is a familiar plant of fens and riversides, though in wetter areas it can also be found in hollows in grasslands. Its yellow flowers are replaced in autumn by dry capsules bearing brown seeds. Flowering period: May-June.

Below: The banks of slow-flowing rivers or backwaters are often very rich in species. Here the water has frogbit (*Hydrocharis morsus-ranae*) floating in it and at the edge both mare's-tail (*Hippuris vulgaris*) and the aroid *Calla palustris*. On the bank itself are the great waterdock (*Rumex hydrolapathum*), cowbane (*Cicuta virosa*) and a variety of grasses and sedges. Flowering period: July-August.

The flowering rush (*Butomus umbellatus*) is perhaps the most beautiful of all waterside plants. The flowers, pink with darker veining, are borne in a simple umbel. It is growing here on a river bank with bulrushes (*Typha* species) in the background. Flowering period: July-September.

reducing the clarity of the water. The earth banks provide a habitat for many plants, most of which help to stabilize them. Fen species, such as meadowsweet (*Filipendula ulmaria*), the great willowherb (*Epilobium hirsutum*) and water figwort (*Scrophularia auriculata*), form a zone high up the bank where they are only occasionally flooded. Nearer the water, there is usually a fringe of reed-swamp plants such as bur-reed, clubrush, grasses such as *Glyceria maxima* and various sedges (*Carex* species) which are sometimes accompanied by the decorative flowering-rush (*Butomus umbellatus*) and arrow-head (*Sagittaria sagittifolia*). If the water is clear, there may be submerged pondweeds, particularly *Potamogeton nodosus*, sometimes accompanied by Canadian waterweed and yellow water-lilies. Arrow-head, clubrush and bur-reed also produce submerged forms, whose flaccid, ribbon-like leaves, offering less resistance to water-flow, look very different from the more familiar erect, stiff aerial leaves. The vegetation of still backwaters and oxbows is like that of the eutrophic pools described earlier.

Artificial water habitats

Many of the waters of north-west Europe are artificial and some provide rich habitats for aquatic plants. The largest are reservoirs. The vegetation of these depends upon the extent to which their level fluctuates: in reservoirs that have a fairly stable water level, the vegetation may be very similar to that in a natural lake, but if the level drops greatly during the year, any aquatic plants in the upper parts of the reservoir are liable to be killed by drought, whilst the deeper parts may not be colonized because they lack light when the level is high.

Flooded quarries can provide excellent plant habitats, although some, such as clay pits, develop slowly because the water is full of clay particles. Canals carry vegetation in inverse relation to boat traffic. Abandoned and little-used canals make outstanding aquatic plant habitats, sometimes with vegetation covering the whole surface, but both submerged and floating vegetation are vulnerable to passing boats: the propellors cut the leaves and also stir up mud which reduces light penetration, while the wash can damage the bank vegetation. However, even in better-used canals, passing places and water reservoirs can support the more resistant water plants. Drainage ditches, although they often remain as a memorial to extensive wetlands, can themselves carry a very rich flora, as in eastern England, Belgium and the Netherlands. The variety of the flora depends upon how often the ditches are cleared and also on the extent to which herbicides are used. All these artificial waters help to some extent to repair the damage caused by man to natural waters through pollution and drainage.

8
Mires:
fens and bogs

A mire is an area of land which is more or less permanently waterlogged but is not open water. Mires occur in a wide range of situations, for instance, around the edges of lakes, in waterlogged hollows, along river flood plains and associated with springs, but all have the same fundamental feature of being wet. Waterlogging reduces the amount of oxygen available for the micro-organisms which normally break down dead plant material. As a result, many mires are peat-producing systems, for peat is made up largely of the accumulated, partially-decomposed remains of the plants that once grew on the mire surface.

Mires formed throughout north-west Europe during the Post-glacial period and came to occupy large areas of land, particularly on low-lying plains. They have now been drastically reduced in extent and number by human settlement and land reclamation but they still remain as conspicuous features in some regions. In parts of Finland they comprise more than 70 per cent of the total land area, and, in many other parts of Fennoscandia, more than half.

Many ecologists distinguish two main types of mire. Minerotrophic mires, or fens, develop under the influence of ground-water, water that has been in contact with the surrounding rock or soil and so has a higher level of dissolved nutrients. In contrast, ombrotrophic mires, or bogs, are irrigated directly and exclusively by rainfall and from this alone they derive their nutrient supply. Since the nutrient content of the water is one of the major factors determining the presence of particular wetland plants, this distinction is reflected in the plants that grow in the mires. Other factors affecting plant growth include the rate of water flow and the rise and fall of the water-table within the mire. All of these factors can interact in a complex way.

A very large number of different plants grow in mires and many of the species are exclusive to such habitats. Like plants

An aapamire in winter with only the tops of the strings appearing above the ice and snow. On the higher ground behind are spruce trees (*Picea abies*).

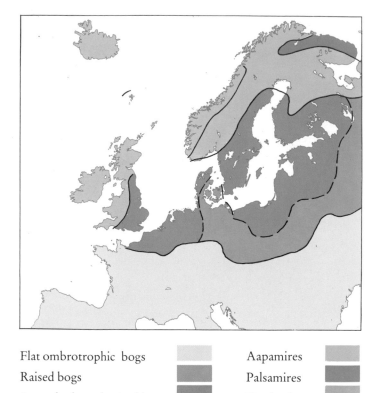

Flat ombrotrophic bogs		Aapamires	
Raised bogs		Palsamires	
Strongly domed raised bogs		Blanket bogs	

Ombrotrophic bogs rely entirely on rainfall for their water and nutrient supplies. This map shows the distribution of the different types of bogs in north-west Europe.

of lake and river habitats, they often have special features that permit them to grow in a waterlogged environment, such as large air canals which extend through their internal tissues. These cavities are probably instrumental in helping to transport oxygen down to the roots. Very many of the mire plants are sedges and rushes but there is also a wide range of other herbaceous species, including some of the most attractive in the European flora.

Minerotrophic mires: fens

FENS AROUND POOLS AND LAKES

Fen vegetation frequently forms a zone of variable extent around open water. It forms part of the hydrosere, the process by which areas of open water develop into mires or even woodlands as plant remains accumulate.

Fen vegetation is preceded by a phase of deeper-water swamp (see Chapter 7). Over much of lowland Europe this swamp is composed of tall, luxuriant grass-like plants, one of the most frequent being the common reed (*Phragmites australis*). Sometimes growing up to 3 m tall and with elegant plumes of flowers, it typically forms a dense and highly productive vegetation. Other swamp plants include the reed-like grass *Glyceria maxima*, the bulrush (*Typha latifolia*) and

the common clubrush (*Scirpus lacustris*), all plants with the same general growth form. In less nutrient-rich conditions and at higher altitudes and latitudes, these species tend to be replaced by smaller plants, particularly sedges, which form a sparser and much less productive swamp vegetation.

Rich fens around pools and lakes After deep-water swamp, the following phase of fen occurs when the surface of the peat reaches nearly to the water surface. In the nutrient-rich fens of the European lowlands, the reed is usually still common and it sometimes remains the dominant plant, forming dense beds which may be regularly mown for thatching and mat-making material. However, a feature of very many fens is the prominence of some of the taller species of sedge. (The term sedge is used here to refer to the true sedges (genus *Carex*) and other members of the same family (Cyperaceae) with a similar growth form.) Tall-sedge fens occur throughout north-west Europe. One of the most widespread types, though absent from the far north, is dominated by tussocks of *Carex elata*. In other fens, *Carex paniculata*, which forms even larger tussocks, or the creeping *C. acuta* or *C. acutiformis* may be prominent. More restricted, though often plentiful where it occurs, is *Cladium mariscus*, a very robust sedge which has fiercely armoured leaves.

Many of the other species growing on tall-sedge fens are equally tall, herbaceous, broad-leaved plants and, together with the sedges these often produce a very colourful vegetation. Typical examples include hemp agrimony (*Eupatorium cannabinum*), tufted loosestrife (*Lysimachia thyrsiflora*), yellow loosestrife (*L. vulgaris*), purple loosestrife (*Lythrum salicaria*), milk-parsley (*Peucedanum palustre*) and, particularly in the more continental fens, fen-ragwort (*Senecio paludosus*). The grasses *Calamagrostis canescens* and *Poa palustris* are often found growing with these and sometimes the small, single, green fronds of the marsh-fern (*Thelypteris thelypteroides*) are abundant as well. Of the various plants that scramble up through the vegetation, marsh-bedstraw (*Galium palustre*) is probably the most widespread. More elegant and less common is the marsh pea (*Lathyrus palustris*). In the wetter parts of the fens, several additional species may appear, often including two umbellifers: the highly poisonous cowbane (*Cicuta virosa*) and the greater water-parsnip (*Sium latifolium*), a very robust plant, sometimes more than 2 m tall. Here, too, may be found the largest European 'buttercup', the greater spearwort (*Ranunculus lingua*), with yellow flowers up to 5 cm across. Fen vegetation such as this occurs not only near open water but also on peaty areas by rivers and streams or in hollows which may once have been open water.

Unless it is artificially extended by regular mowing or grazing, the fen phase of the hydrosere is often rather short-lived. As peat continues to accumulate, conditions become

Rich fens have many attractive flowers. Here purple loosestrife (*Lythrum salicaria*) grows with yellow loosestrife (*Lysimachia vulgaris*). In spite of their common names these two plants are not closely related. Purple loosestrife is in the family Lythraceae whereas yellow is a member of the Primulaceae, the primrose family. Flowering period: June-August.

The marsh pea (*Lathyrus palustris*) is particularly characteristic of fens, where it is found climbing up the taller vegetation. The flowers are quite large, about 18mm, and are borne in groups at the end of a long stalk. Flowering period: May-July.

drier and trees are able to invade, so that the herbaceous fen is replaced by mire forest. The first woody invaders are trees tolerant of waterlogging such as alder *(Alnus glutinosa)* and various willows *(Salix* species). As the ground rises even higher, these may be supplemented by trees of the drier deciduous woodlands such as ash *(Fraxinus excelsior)* and pedunculate oak *(Quercus robur)*.

In many areas where there is comparatively high rainfall, peat may accumulate above the mineral ground-water. As it becomes increasingly isolated from this nutrient source, it becomes more acidic. Such sites are often marked by the appearance of patches of bog moss (*Sphagnum* species).

Poor fens around pools and lakes Fens which develop around waters that are poorer in dissolved nutrients are characterized by a different range of species. The main sedges are often *Carex rostrata* and *C. lasiocarpa* and, in the north, *Carex aquatilis*, frequently mingled with common cottongrass (*Eriophorum angustifolium*). Cottongrasses (*Eriophorum* species) are easily recognized by their white, cottony fruiting heads. *E. angustifolium* has several nodding heads and, even when not in fruit, can usually be identified by its isolated shoots with glossy green leaves which turn red towards the tips. Two characteristic and common associates are marsh cinquefoil (*Potentilla palustris*) and bogbean (*Menyanthes trifoliata*). Bogbean has flowers among the most attractive of all wetland plants. It also has buoyant rhizomes that sometimes form a raft on the open water. In general, tall herbs are not as prominent as they are in the richer fens, though tufted loosestrife may sometimes occur. Smaller species such as marsh-willowherb (*Epilobium palustre*) and marsh-violet (*Viola palustris*) are frequent however, often with other sedges such as *Carex nigra*. In much of Fennoscandia and in parts of eastern Europe, *Carex chordorrhiza* and *C. magellanica* are also frequent. In Iceland, *Carex lyngbyei*, a sedge which also occurs in the Faeroes but nowhere else in Europe, is both characteristic and abundant. The vegetation is often rather short and not very dense and, partly in response to this, mosses are often luxuriant. Species of *Sphagnum* are particularly common and may sometimes form an almost continuous carpet. Frequently creeping over this are the long, trailing shoots of cranberry (*Vaccinium oxycoccos*), with their large edible red berries, and in some places the small green spikes of the bog orchid (*Hammarbya paludosa*) can also be found—though often only with some difficulty.

A rather interesting hydrosere can sometimes be seen around small, deep, steep-sided pools such as those occupying glacial kettle-holes (hollows left by the melting of blocks of ice buried in glacial debris). Here, instead of sediments collecting and filling the lake basin from below, a floating skin of vegetation and accumulating peat develops out over the surface of the water. This type of mire is known as a schwingmoor. Although at first the vegetation raft is thin, unstable and highly treacherous, it gradually becomes firmer and more stable as peat continues to build up. One of the most widespread types of schwingmoor is found in deep, stagnant hollows containing nutrient-poor water. In these acidic conditions, the raft is composed largely of *Sphagnum*

Cottongrasses are usually found on bogs and in poor fens but *Eriophorum latifolium* is characteristic of rich fens. It is tufted and has from two to twelve cottony heads on every flowering stem. These are the fruiting heads, which develop about a month later than the flowers. Flowering period: May-June.

Right: The cranberry *Vaccinium oxycoccos* is a small, trailing plant with narrow oval leaves. It is usually found on the open, mossy areas of poor fens and bogs. It has remarkably large, shiny, red fruits that are ripe from August to October and are very good to eat. Flowering period: June-August.

bound together by the entwining rhizomes of common cottongrass or, sometimes, the sedge *Carex lasiocarpa*. A frequent feature of these *Sphagnum* lawns is an abundance of the sundew *Drosera rotundifolia*, sometimes so plentiful that its reddish colour largely masks the green of the *Sphagnum*. This plant, like several other wetland species, is insectivorous. Its leaves, covered by sticky glands, can capture insects and digest them using enzymes secreted by the glands. The sundew absorbs some of the products from its decaying victims and so supplements its own meagre nutrient supply. The sedges *Rhynchospora alba* and *Carex limosa*, both plants which seem to favour the wettest areas of mires, also occur frequently, while, in the firmer parts, bog rosemary (*Andromeda polifolia*) may be found. This acid-

Left: Bog bean (*Menyanthes trifoliata*) is one of the most attractive plants of the poorest fens and of bog pools. The stems and rhizomes are buoyant so that the plant can grow out over open water to give a treacherous, floating surface. Flowering period: May-July.

The sundew (*Drosera rotundifolia*) is often found growing on the surface of bog moss (*Sphagnum*). It is thought to supplement its meagre nutrient supply by trapping insects with its special moveable, sticky hairs and obtaining extra nourishment from their bodies. Several small white flowers, which do not usually open, appear at the top of a long, slender flowering stalk. Flowering period: June-August.

Below: A section across a schwingmoor showing the vegetation and peat raft floating on the surface of the water, with only a small area of open water. The lake basin slowly fills with organic remains, especially near the edges.

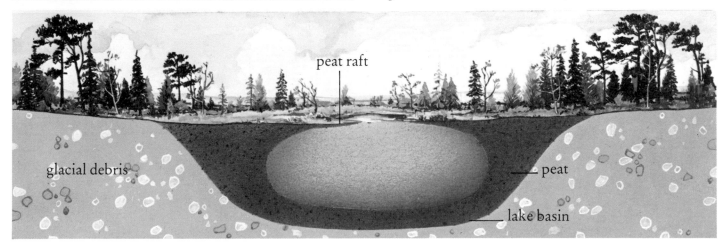

glacial debris   peat raft   peat   lake basin

loving type of vegetation has obvious similarities to that of the ombrotrophic mires or bogs (see below) into which, in fact, it may develop. However, the occurrence of plants such as the sedge *Carex curta* indicates clearly that the peat is still being supplied with mineral-enriched water. This kind of vegetation, a form of poor fen, is by no means confined exclusively to schwingmoor. It can also occur elsewhere, such as around the edges of bogs, where, although wet, it is not necessarily floating.

As peat accumulates, the surface of the schwingmoor becomes drier and trees are able to invade. Downy birch *(Betula pubescens)* and Scots pine *(Pinus sylvestris)* are the usual colonizing species. The raft of peat cannot always support the increasing weight of growing trees. In such circumstances the trees may gradually sink through the raft and, as the roots are submerged, become moribund and die.

FENS ASSOCIATED WITH SPRINGS AND FLUSHES

In contrast to the series of fens described above are those that usually develop on slopes, sometimes very slight ones, under the influence of flowing water. They often occur below springs and areas of water seepage (flushes). The irrigating water may vary greatly in the composition and content of dissolved salts. It may be very rich in minerals and have a fairly high pH, or it may be very poor in minerals and acidic. As with fens around pools and lakes, these varying conditions give rise to rich and poor fens respectively.

Calcareous fens Calcareous fens are distinguished from other rich fens in having water that is particularly rich in calcium. They are widely distributed throughout north-west Europe, but largely confined, of course, to areas with a substratum rich in lime. They vary in size from small fragments surrounding a calcareous spring to some of the huge fens of central Sweden, and they occur at all altitudes.

One of the most distinctive features of calcareous fens is that they are often very rich in plant species, a number of which are rare or uncommon. Such fens are therefore of exceptional botanical interest. The predominant species are still usually sedges. Over much of the European lowlands the sedge *Schoenus nigricans* is often one of the most abundant plants, though in Fennoscandia and the mountains of central Europe it is partly replaced by its close relative *S. ferrugineus*. This is often accompanied by *Scirpus hudsonianus* which, like the cottongrasses, has white, cottony fruits. Taller species, such as the reed and the sedge *Cladium mariscus*, occur in some fens but often only as scattered individuals. Instead, it is the smaller plants that tend to predominate. *Carex lepidocarpa, C. flacca, C. panicea, C. nigra* and *Eriophorum latifolium* are all very characteristic in calcareous fens. The rush *Juncus articulatus* is common and *J. subnodulosus* often occurs, though not in the far north.

The small pink flowers of the bog rosemary (*Andromeda polifolia*) are not always easy to see, but the dark leaves which surround them have a distinctive, pale patterning. Bog rosemary is usually found in poor fens and particularly in raised bogs, often growing, as here, with sundews. Flowering period: May-September.

Various aquatic plants grow in pools in fens and bogs. One example is the bladderwort *Utricularia vulgaris* which is here growing in a ditch within a rich fen. Bladderworts are free floating and have only submerged leaves with small bladders which act as traps, catching small aquatic animals. As the animals decompose they add to the nutrient supply of the plants. Flowering period: July-August.

Left: The distinctive flowers of grass of Parnassus (*Parnassia vulgaris*) have, inside the ring of white petals, five groups of 7 to 15 needle-like points, tipped with round, yellowish glands. Between each group is a single normal stamen. Flowering period: July-October.

Though sedges are the dominant species, it is the rich variety of smaller herbs that is a particular feature of calcareous fens. Common examples include water mint (*Mentha aquatica*), devil's-bit scabious (*Succisa pratensis*) and marsh valerian (*Valeriana dioica*), along with the semi-parasitic marsh lousewort (*Pedicularis palustris*), which derives at least some of its food from the roots of other wetland plants, and common butterwort (*Pinguicula vulgaris*), which augments its food supply by the insects that stick to the greasy surface of its broad, yellowish leaves. Grass-of-Parnassus (*Parnassia palustris*), with its white chalice-like flowers, is often conspicuous in late summer. Orchids are also well represented, two of the most widespread being the early marsh-orchid (*Dactylorhiza incarnata*) and marsh-helleborine (*Epipactis palustris*).

These fens are generally developed on a wet, oozing peat, but drier areas occur along their edges or on hummocks created by the vegetation itself. Such areas can frequently be picked out by abundant tussocks of purple moor-grass (*Molinia caerulea*) or even, chiefly in eastern parts of Fennoscandia and eastern Germany, by the grass *Sesleria caerulea*. Species of drier habitats such as fairy flax (*Linum catharticum*) and tormentil (*Potentilla erecta*) gain a foothold in such places and are sometimes accompanied by the fragrant orchid (*Gymnadenia conopsea*) and, less often, by the fly orchid (*Ophrys insectifera*) and the military orchid (*Orchis militaris*). Other parts may be much wetter. Open, muddy runnels often contain the spike-rush *Eleocharis quinqueflora*, marsh arrowgrass (*Triglochin palustris*) and sometimes the horsetail *Equisetum variegatum*, while small pools support aquatic plants such as the pondweed *Potamogeton coloratus* or species of bladderwort (*Utricularia*). Many calcareous fens consist, therefore, of an intricate mosaic of microhabitats. Although rich in species and certain nutrients such as calcium, such fens, like many calcareous habitats, are often poor in nitrogen and phosphorus and tend to be infertile.

Various bushes invade calcareous fens. The more important plants include alder, alder buckthorn (*Frangula alnus*) and species of birch and willow, such as grey willow (*Salix cinerea*), *S. aurita* (often in slightly more acid situations) and bay willow (*S. pentandra*), especially in the north and east. Scots pine and juniper (*Juniperus communis*) sometimes grow in the drier parts of the more northern fens. Smaller shrubs such as the creeping willow (*Salix repens*) also often occur. The dwarf birch (*Betula nana*), a very widespread shrub of mires in Fennoscandia, is plentiful in the rich fens of this region, but is replaced around the southern parts of the Baltic Sea and in eastern Germany by another small species of birch, *Betula humilis*.

In depressions and on very gentle slopes, where there is

The small leaves of the bog pimpernel (*Anagallis tenella*) are inconspicuous, but its delicate pink flowers with their attractive patterning allow immediate identification. It is found in open areas of the richer fens. Flowering period: June-August.

Right: *Bartsia alpina* is a perennial of mountain fens. Its dull purple flowers are borne amongst purple-green bracts at the top of the stems and are often inconspicuous. Flowering period: June-August.

often a high, rather stagnant, water-table, certain other plants can be found in addition to many of those already mentioned. The sedge *Carex lasiocarpa*, although widespread in various types of mire, is typically very abundant here, with *C. limosa* in the wettest parts. The slightly tufted *C. diandra* may also occur, often with another species of cottongrass, *Eriophorum gracile*. The small yellowish-green spikes of the fen orchid (*Liparis loeselii*) are frequently found in this type of fen. As in other areas of rich fen, bryophytes, particularly the straggling mat-forming mosses, are characteristically plentiful.

Calcareous fens show quite pronounced regional differences throughout north-west Europe. In the British Isles, for example, and in parts of western France, the bog pimpernel (*Anagallis tenella*), with its long, trailing shoots and pale pink flowers, is frequent, often with the spineless thistle *Cirsium dissectum* and the water-dropwort *Oenanthe lachenalii*. The marsh orchid *Dactylorhiza majalis* subsp. *praetermissa* occurs in fens in southern Britain, while subsp. *purpurella* replaces it farther north. Both orchids are very oceanic and only grow in a very few places on the European mainland, where Atlantic species generally become increasingly rare towards the east and others take their place. These include *Orchis laxiflora* subsp. *palustris* and the umbellifer *Selinum carvifolia*, a plant very similar to the closely related milk-parsley. In a few places particularly in parts of France and southern Germany, the rare summer lady's-tresses (*Spiranthes aestivalis*) can still be found.

The sedge *Carex davalliana* and the fragrant orchid *Gymnadenia odoratissima* occur in a few lowland fens, the latter particularly on the Baltic island of Gotland. Both are scattered through lowland Germany but are more abundant in central Europe, particularly in the higher fens of the Alps where they often grow together. Sometimes the yellowish or, more rarely, pink flowering spikes of the musk orchid (*Herminium monorchis*) can be found with them, as well as the asphodel *Tofieldia calyculata*.

A number of species grow both in calcareous fens in the mountains of central Europe and at lower altitudes further north, although they are missing from much of the intervening lowland area. A good example is the pink-flowered bird's-eye primrose (*Primula farinosa*) which has a distribution similar to that of the grass *Sesleria caerulea* and can be found in the Alps, along the southern Baltic coast, in a small area of northern England and in the eastern part of southern Sweden. Another is *Bartsia alpina* which is widespread in Fennoscandia.

Some of the best examples of calcareous fens in the north are found in Jämtland, Sweden. These usually contain species such as *Saussurea alpina*, alpine bistort (*Polygonum*

Fen meadows may be full of a variety of tall herbs similar to those of very damp grasslands. Meadowsweet (*Filipendula ulmaria*) is the dominant flower in this meadow. Flowering period: June–September.

viviparum) and alpine meadow-rue *(Thalictrum alpinum)*. Others include marsh saxifrage *(Saxifraga hirculus)* and Scottish asphodel *(Tofieldia pusilla)*. In some sites the lousewort *Pedicularis sceptrum-carolinum*, a tall, elegant plant with pale yellow flowers, is conspicuous. Cranberry and the dwarf birch are common and another small shrub which, interestingly, occurs here is the bog rosemary, a plant otherwise restricted to acid fens and to bogs in more central and western parts of our area. Towards the edges of the fen there is sometimes a sparsely wooded zone with scattered trees of birch, pine and spruce *(Picea abies)*. These areas are very rich in tall herbs including the hawksbeard *Crepis paludosa*, melancholy thistle *(Cirsium helenioides)*, water avens *(Geum rivale)*, wood cranes-bill *(Geranium sylvaticum)* and globeflower *(Trollius europaeus)*. The round-leaved wintergreen *(Pyrola rotundifolia)* is sometimes abundant, too. Other plants occasionally found in the more northerly Swedish fens include one of the most attractive and uncommon plants of Europe, the lady's-slipper orchid *(Cypripedium calceolus)* and one of the least spectacular, the one-leaved bog orchid *Microstylis monophyllos*.

Although several species of lowland calcareous fens occur at a wide range of altitudes, some of the high-level fens in Norway, Sweden and Scotland have their own distinctive flora. At this altitude, peat formation is less active, partly because the low temperatures greatly reduce plant growth, and the fens often have appreciable areas of exposed mineral soil. Two of the most characteristic plants are *Carex atrofusca* and *C. microglochin*. Other frequent sedges are *C. atrata, C. capillaris, C. saxatilis* and *Kobresia simpliciuscula*. The almost horizontal *Carex bicolor* is an uncommon plant but very characteristic of this type of habitat in Fennoscandia. The small rush *Juncus biglumis* is frequent, sometimes growing with the superficially similar *J. triglumis*. Occurring very commonly with them is the attractive yellow saxifrage *(Saxifraga aizoides)*. Its relative, the early-flowering purple saxifrage *(Saxifraga oppositifolia)*, may occur as well. Butterwort, alpine bistort, alpine meadow-rue and Scottish asphodel are all common, sometimes, in Fennoscandia, with the yellow-flowered lousewort *Pedicularis oederi*. The yellowish-white-flowered butterwort *Pinguicula alpina* grows chiefly in northern Fennoscandia. In the drier parts of the fens, or at the edges, plants such as mountain avens *(Dryas octopetala)* and the gentian *Gentiana nivalis* sometimes grow, and, in Iceland, the orchid *Platanthera hyperborea*. A feature of certain sites is the prominence of small shrubs. In addition to the dwarf birch there are many dwarf willows—such as least willow *(Salix herbacea), S. myrsinites, S. reticulata* and, especially frequent, *S. lapponum*.

113

In conclusion, it is worth mentioning that many rich fens contain small acidic areas. These often arise when moss hummocks grow above the calcareous ground-water, so permitting calcifuge plants, particularly species of *Sphagnum*, to become established close to calcicoles. Large hummocks of *Sphagnum fuscum* are particularly noticeable in these mixed mires.

Poor fens associated with springs and flushes When the irrigating water is poor in minerals, a kind of poor fen occurs which is very similar to the poor fens around lakes and pools. In fact all the fen and bog types tend to merge gradually into one another, so that no rigid distinctions can be made.

The vegetation of these particular poor fens often looks superficially very similar to that of calcareous fens, with a general preponderance of small sedges and a frequently well-developed moss layer, but there are many differences in the species composition. In poor fens, as well as the very common *Carex nigra* and *C. panicea*, other common sedges include *C. rostrata* and *C. lasiocarpa*. *Carex curta* and *C. echinata* are also widespread and characteristic poor-fen species, especially in the slightly more mineral-rich sites. Common associates include marsh willowherb, cottongrass, marsh lousewort, lesser spearwort *(Ranunculus flammula)* and marsh violet. The small rush *Juncus bulbosus* is sometimes abundant. *Sphagnum* species often make up most of the moss cover. Together, these plants tend to produce a rather drab vegetation.

Some of the best examples of this type of poor fen are along the Atlantic seaboard. In the most oceanic areas, especially in western Britain, Ireland and France, the flora is enriched by three creeping plants: the bog pimpernel, lesser skullcap *(Scutellaria minor)* and marsh St John's wort *(Hypericum elodes)*, the last very distinctive with its densely hairy leaves and bright yellow flowers. Two species of butterwort also occur, though in a restricted area. The large and striking *Pinguicula grandiflora* is confined in our region to south-west Ireland whilst the diminutive *P. lusitanica*, although more widespread, is still very much restricted to the western coasts of France and the British Isles. More widespread still, but again very characteristic of Atlantic poor fens, are the rush *Juncus acutiflorus* (sometimes the dominant species), the bog asphodel *(Narthecium ossifragum)* whose yellow-orange flowering spikes form a prominent feature of some of the fens in August, and cross-leaved heath *(Erica tetralix)*. Cross-leaved heath is typical of wet heath (see Chapter 5) but also grows in a range of wetland habitats in the Atlantic area. None of these species grows in the more continental poor fens which often feature tufted loosestrife and milk-parsley. Sedges such as *Carex chordorrhiza*, *C. magellanica* and *C. vaginata* occur in many northern poor fens.

In the more mineral-deficient poor fens, the sedges *Carex*

A mixed mire with large tussocks of *Sphagnum fuscum* providing an acid environment in the middle of a rich fen dominated by the sedge *Carex lasiocarpa*. The shrubs are dwarf birch *(Betula nana)*.

rostrata and *C. lasiocarpa* may coexist with plants typical of bogs. Such poor fens may occupy large areas within the extensive northern peatland complexes and often consist of very few species. Two commonly present are deergrass *(Scirpus cespitosus)* and the cottongrass *Eriophorum vaginatum*. Both are tussock-forming sedges with tough, wiry leaves and the former, as its name suggests, is heavily grazed by deer. In Fennoscandia, bog rosemary and dwarf birch also usually occur and, in the wetter parts, *Carex limosa* and *Scheuchzeria palustris* may be abundant. *Scheuchzeria* is a curious, rush-like plant with undistinguished yellowish flowers and tubular leaves which have a very distinctive small pore at the tip.

In northern Fennoscandia, within the Arctic Circle, *Carex rotundata* is a characteristic poor-fen sedge, often found growing with *C. aquatilis*, *C. nigra* and *C. livida*. Dwarf shrubs are often prominent and include the ubiquitous dwarf birch, the bog bilberry *(Vaccinium uliginosum)* and willows such as *Salix glauca*, *S. lapponum* and tea willow *(S. phylicifolia)*. Associated herbaceous plants include species such as alpine bistort and marsh violet. Similar vegetation

The bog bilberry (*Vaccinium uliginosum*) has probably the most delicious fruits of all the berry-bearing heaths. They are rather larger and rounder than those of the common bilberry (*Vaccinium myrtillus*) and are borne on brown stems with blueish-green leaves. The flowers are pale pink and grow in groups of up to four in the axils of the leaves. Flowering period: May-June.

The yellow flowers and very hairy, greyish-green leaves of the marsh St. John's wort (*Hypericum elodes*) make it easily recognizable as it grows in the more open, wetter parts of the poor fens in the west of the region. The hairs prevent the plant from getting wet even when the leaves are submerged. Flowering period: June-September.

Right: *Pedicularis sceptrum-carolinum* is a perennial lousewort most commonly found in the fens of Fennoscandia. It is most easily identified by its flowers, which have a yellow lower lip with a red margin. Flowering period: July.

occurs in parts of Iceland and includes the sedge *Carex lyngbyei*. In the mountains of Fennoscandia, poor fens often feature the sedges *Carex bigelowii* and *C. rariflora* and the cottongrass *Eriophorum scheuchzeri*, although these plants may also occur at lower altitudes. The cottongrass is often a pioneer species of very open habitats where it frequently grows with the grass *Calamagrostis stricta*. Other plants of montane poor fens include the dwarf willow and grasses such as *Poa alpina*. A number of these plants also grow in mountain areas south of the Arctic Circle; some occur in Scotland and others reappear in the mountains of central Europe.

In the more oceanic areas of the Atlantic coasts, in the British Isles, Faeroes and western Scandinavia, poor-fen vegetation alongside streams and in the soakaways of upland mires characteristically has purple moor-grass and bog-myrtle *(Myrica gale)*. Bog-myrtle is a pleasantly aromatic, low-growing shrub with the capacity to use atmospheric nitrogen, which is presumably why it thrives in these nutrient deficient soils. Sometimes these two may be the only plants present.

FEN MEADOWS

Fen meadows are derived from fens by grazing or mowing and contain a mixture of plants typical of fens and grasslands. Although often small in extent, they are very widespread, occurring in agricultural landscapes throughout north-west Europe, where they are often grazed and trampled by livestock and subject to some degree of manuring. This management is important for keeping such fen meadows low growing and in its absence they would probably revert to other types of fen. In some areas of the European lowlands, as, for example, in much of southern Britain, fen meadows are almost the only kind of mire vegetation that remains.

Rushes are often very conspicuous in fen meadows, *Juncus subnodulosus* in the most nutrient-rich sites and *J. acutiflorus* and *J. effusus* where nutrients are in shorter supply. *Juncus inflexus* also often occurs, reliably indicating the strong influence of the mineral soil, for many of these fens have only a shallow layer of peat. Also conspicuous are the sedges *Carex acutiformis* and *C. disticha*, together with various fen and wet-meadow herbs such as angelica *(Angelica sylvestris)*, marsh marigold *(Caltha palustris)*, marsh thistle *(Cirsium palustre)* and also *C. oleraceum*, hoary willowherb *(Epilobium parviflorum)*, meadowsweet *(Filipendula ulmaria)*, square-stemmed St John's-wort *(Hypericum tetrapterum)*, marsh bird's-foot-trefoil *(Lotus uliginosus)* and ragged-robin *(Lychnis flos-cuculi)*. Grasses such as creeping bent *(Agrostis stolonifera)*, red fescue *(Festuca rubra)*, Yorkshire-fog *(Holcus lanatus)* and the meadow-grass *Poa trivialis* are often common, though rarely forming a

A rich fen on sloping ground, dominated by purple moor-grass *(Molinia caerulea)*. The fen is surrounded by subalpine birch woods with an undergrowth of dwarf shrubs.

Right: In many bogs erosion of peat occurs. Here a peat ridge colonized by dwarf birch *(Betula nana)* is eroding on one margin and the bare peat areas at the lower level are being colonized by hummocks of the moss *Rhacomitrium lanuginosum* and sedges.

continuous turf. Other herbs include common mouse-ear *(Cerastium fontanum)*, meadow buttercup *(Ranunculus acris)* and sorrel *(Rumex acetosa)*.

In the north and east, these plants are often supplemented by larger herbs, such as the hawksbeard *Crepis paludosa*, water avens and globeflower. By contrast, water figwort *(Scrophularia auriculata)* is largely confined to the south and west, where it may be frequent. In this area, nutrient-poor fen meadows may also contain lesser skullcap and the delicate ivy-leaved bellflower *(Wahlenbergia hederacea)*.

Ombrotrophic mires: bogs

Bogs are ombrotrophic wetlands, relying entirely on rainfall for their water and nutrient supply. They are therefore

characteristically very poor in nutrients. The plants *par excellence* of ombrotrophic mires in north-west Europe are the bog mosses *(Sphagnum* species). These plants thrive in highly acidic conditions and, indeed, produce organic substances which actually increase the acidity of their surroundings. They constitute the bulk of bog vegetation and are largely responsible for the huge deposits of peat that have accumulated in many of the mires.

RAISED BOGS

Within north-west Europe there are two main types of bogs—raised bogs and blanket bogs. Raised bogs are the most widely distributed type, sometimes, but by no means always, developing over fens as ombrotrophic peat accumulates above the level of the minerotrophic ground-water. They depend upon a favourable balance between precipitation and evaporation to maintain the surface in a waterlogged condition, so making it possible for peat to continue to accumulate. They are therefore restricted to comparatively cool, wet climates. *Sphagnum* is ideally suited as a basis for raised bog formation because much of the plant, particularly the leaves, consists of large, dead cells which can

A small raised bog has a domed shape, surrounded by a moat-like lagg. In section it is shown occupying a hollow in boulder clay. The bottom layer of the bog is formed of materials deposited while it was a lake, covered by a layer of fen peat from the stage when all the vegetation was affected by the mineral-rich ground water. On the top is a layer of bog peat, laid down as the centre of the bog was raised above the influence of the ground waters and so became dependent on nutrients from air and rainfall.

lagg
bog peat
fen peat
lake sediments
lagg
boulder clay

hold considerable quantities of water. Both the living plants and their dead remains act, therefore, as an enormous sponge and give rise to a dome of peat, fully charged with water, raised up above the level of the original ground-water table. The height which the dome can reach largely depends on the size of the mire and the precipitation-evaporation balance. The highest examples are in oceanic western areas where domes may exceed 6m. In less oceanic areas, only a shallow dome or flat surface can be produced. Surrounding the raised bog is the moat-like lagg. This receives enriched water from the soil and rocks of the surrounding area and it generally supports a poor-fen vegetation, though in some sites, where the lagg is fed by calcareous springs, good rich-fen vegetation may develop.

Raised bogs were once very extensive in north-west Europe, particularly in the lowlands. Nowadays many of these have been cut for peat or even completely reclaimed so that good examples are infrequent. The intact surface of a raised bog usually has *Sphagnum* as the predominant plant together with various sedges, some dwarf shrubs and several herbs. The numerous species of *Sphagnum* may appear difficult to distinguish from one another but in fact some of the main bog-building species are easy to recognize. *Sphagnum magellanicum* and *S. capillifolium*, two important species, are both typically dark crimson but *S. magellanicum* is much more robust and, with its swollen leafy branches, is easily distinguished. Both tend to form actively growing hummocks, though *S. nemoreum*, which is able to survive in some of the driest parts of the bog can often be found capping the hummocks of other *Sphagnum* species. Another common bog moss, often forming low hummocks, is *S. subnitens*, a variable plant often coloured pink, with a bluish metallic sheen that is particularly conspicuous when the plant is dry.

On many, though by no means all bogs, the *Sphagnum* hummocks occur close together and form a characteristic system of hummocks and hollows. The hummock tops grow more slowly and provide the driest and most acid micro-habitat, tending to be crowned with lichens and dwarf shrubs such as heather *(Calluna vulgaris)*. Amongst the hummocks are much wetter hollows, sometimes with open pools. Grass-green carpets of *Sphagnum recurvum* are often found in the hollows or sometimes form extensive lawns. The wettest places, however, are usually occupied by *S. cuspidatum*, a rather bedraggled, dull-green species which often grows submerged in bog pools, where, throughout much of north-west Europe, it is accompanied by *Carex limosa*, *Rhynchospora alba* and *Scheuchzeria palustris*.

Other species typical of raised bogs include bog-rosemary, cranberry and sundew. Sedges are well represented by tussocks of the cottongrass *Eriophorum vaginatum* and

Among the plants growing on this hummock of *Sphagnum fuscum* on a raised bog are the large roundish leaves of cloudberry *(Rubus chamaemorus)*, small shrubs of dwarf birch *(Betula nana)* and the narrow leaves of bog rosemary *(Andromeda polifolia)*.

deergrass, although the only true sedges found widely in bogs are *Carex limosa* and the small *C. pauciflora*.

In general, raised bogs in the more oceanic west are treeless, and support several plant species that are not found farther east. One of the main bog-building species is *Sphagnum papillosum*, a robust plant that forms large, ochre-coloured hummocks. Another, *Sphagnum imbricatum*, which forms large brownish hummocks, is also largely confined to Atlantic bogs. Though known to have been an important peat-forming species in the past, it is now rare. Cross-leaved heath and the sundew *Drosera intermedia* are also often present. It is interesting that western bogs contain several species which, further east, are strictly confined to minerotrophic fens. This could be because in the west there is a higher rate of water flow through the bogs. Such species include the cottongrass *Eriophorum angustifolium* and purple moor-grass, as well as certain *Sphagnum* species. In eastern parts of Scandinavia, for example, oceanic raised-bog species such as *Sphagnum imbricatum* and *S. papillosum* do occur, but only in poor-fen vegetation.

Farther east, towards the more continental areas of Fennoscandia and Germany, the appearance of the raised bog changes and there are different species, *Sphagnum fuscum* being especially characteristic. The large, golden-brown mounds of this moss can be found in some oceanic bogs, but

In June, many bogs are covered by the fluffy white fruiting heads of species of cottongrass *Eriophorum*. The silky hairs are the equivalent of the sepals and petals of other flowers, but do not develop until the fruit has set.

it is most abundant in the east. There is an increasing tendency eastwards for raised bogs to be wooded, the tree cover usually being Scots pine. At first the trees are generally round the edge, with only scattered, stunted individuals in the wettest parts, but in the most easterly bogs the tree cover may be complete.

In Fennoscandia, both wooded and non-wooded raised bogs occur. The northern dwarf birch and cloudberry (*Rubus chamaemorus*) are characteristic of both types. Cloudberry is a small creeping plant with white flowers and delightfully edible orange-yellow berries that are often collected and sold in local markets. The woods usually have a dwarf shrub layer which includes heather, crowberry (*Empetrum nigrum*), Labrador tea (*Ledum palustre*), *Chamaedaphne calyculata* (chiefly in Finland), and four species of *Vaccinium*—bog-bilberry, cranberry and, in the drier parts only, bilberry (*V. myrtillus*) and cowberry (*V. vitis-idaea*). *Carex globularis* is a very characteristic sedge of wooded bog margins in eastern Fennoscandia. Very similar types of mire forest occur on some Fennoscandian poor fens.

In Fennoscandia, the principal area of raised bog is in the south though in suitable conditions, examples may also be found further north, their flora including much *Sphagnum fuscum*, dwarf birch, cloudberry and *Vaccinium microcarpum*. This last species closely resembles cranberry

The most characteristic plants of bogs are the bog-mosses, *Sphagnum* species. Both stems and leaves have many large dead cells, linked with the outside through pores, so that the whole plant acts like a sponge and can absorb large quantities of water.

but has smaller fruits. At these higher latitudes and in the mountains, trees tend to be less frequent and heather is often completely absent. An interesting plant found on hummocks in some of the subarctic bogs is the butterwort *Pinguicula villosa*, a tiny plant, with leaves often less than 10mm long.

BLANKET BOGS

Blanket bogs, so called because they cover the ground like a blanket, are a feature of the highly oceanic areas of western Europe, particularly the British Isles. They occur mainly in the uplands, where the balance between precipitation and evaporation is such that rainfall keeps even sloping ground in a permanently wet condition. The vegetation of good examples of blanket bog is rather similar to that of the western raised bogs, with cloudberry and cowberry occurring in some of the more northerly sites. In some areas, however, large tracts of blanket bog have become degraded into heather moor, or are covered with the cottongrass *Eriophorum vaginatum* with very few other species. This may be partly a result of heavy sheep-grazing and burning but it is possible, particularly downwind of industrial areas, that atmospheric pollution by sulphur dioxide may also have had some effect.

Blanket bogs are especially well developed in Ireland where they cover enormous areas, occurring even on slopes of up to 25°, and on limestone. An interesting feature of some of the most western examples is the abundance of the sedge *Schoenus nigricans*, usually a rich-fen species, sometimes with the butterworts *Pinguicula vulgaris* and *P. lusitanica*.

Aapamires

Over much of Fennoscandia, particularly on the extensive plains in the north, aapamires constitute the main type of mire. These are usually very large, slightly sloping systems, characterized by a very distinctive surface patterning in which, more or less at right angles to the slope, numerous interlocking peat ridges, or strings, cross the mire. They are separated by an equally large number of flat, very wet depressions, or flarks, which are often so wide, deep and treacherous that they are impossible to cross. It is thought they are created by the vast quantities of water that flow through the mires when the snow melts in spring. This highlights one of the most important features of these mires, namely that although their water may be very poor in nutrients so that many bog species occur, they are nevertheless irrigated at least in part by minerotrophic water and must be regarded as fen systems. Even the string vegetation is often flooded by the high spring waters and it is only on the highest strings and in the marginal areas that true ombrotrophic vegetation can be found. The higher strings

This aapamire has its peaty ridges dominated by dwarf birch (*Betula nana*) and the cottongrass *Eriophorum vaginatum*, with occasional pine trees. The intervening flarks (open water) are colonized by the sedge *Carex livida*.

support species such as cloudberry, bog-rosemary, cranberry, the cottongrass *Eriophorum vaginatum* and the bog moss *Sphagnum fuscum*, while purple moor-grass and the sedge *Carex lasiocarpa* grow on the lower ones.

The vegetation of the flarks is very interesting though sometimes difficult to examine. In the more nutrient-rich flarks, sedges are usually prominent, as for example *Carex limosa*, *C. rostrata*, *C. chordorrhiza*, *C. livida* and *Eriophorum angustifolium*. Also frequent are the sundew *Drosera anglica*, bogbean *Scheuchzeria palustris*, and, in the north, the rush *Juncus stygius* and the cottongrass *Eriophorum russeolum*. Mires irrigated by the richest water have a number of additional species including *Eriophorum latifolium* and Scottish asphodel. Many flarks support an extensive growth of quaking *Sphagnum* carpets but others may be open areas of water, the muddy bottoms of which are wholly or partially covered by a film of algae and have only a small amount of moss. There is usually only a very sparse cover of flowering plants.

Cloudberry (*Rubus chamaemorus*) is a bramble which has its stems underground and only the leaves and flowers above the surface. The leaves are rounded, with 5 to 7 lobes and are crinkly on the surface. The flowers are similar to those of the blackberry. The delicious fruit is again like a blackberry but is orange when ripe. Flowering period: June-August.

Chamaedaphne calyculata is a small ericaceous shrub of the poor fens and bogs of the north east of the region. It is closely related to bog rosemary *(Andromeda polifolia)* and can easily be distinguished by its pendant white flowers and the leaves covered with brown scales beneath. Flowering period: July.

Aapamires also occur in Iceland. There, the strings usually support a shrubby vegetation with dwarf birch, crowberry, bog bilberry and various willows. Bog-rosemary, cloud-berry, and the cottongrass *Eriophorum vaginatum* are, however, completely absent and cranberry is rare.

Palsamires

Palsamires occur to the north of the aapamires, in the region where parts of the ground at least are permanently frozen. *Palsa* is a Finnish word which refers to ridges and mounds within bogs. These large mounds, up to 10m tall, contain a permanently frozen core of peat and silt. The surface layer melts in the summer and the plants then grow, adding to the peat and providing insulation which keeps the core frozen. As they grow the palsas may merge to form extensive ridges or raised areas. The vegetation consists mainly of plants characteristic of bogs but some poor-fen species may grow in the hollows between the palsas.

9
Saltmarshes and reclaimed land

Salt marshes develop where the physical structure of the coast below the level of the extreme high spring tides provides sufficiently shallow and sheltered conditions for land plants to grow. These conditions are to be found in the mouths of estuaries, in sheltered bays, on coasts protected by offshore islands, dune ridges, or shingle spits, and within land reclaimed from the sea. Salt marshes, therefore, tend to be scattered all round the north-west European coast. They vary greatly in extent, some covering many hundreds of hectares, sloping gently seawards so that their uniform appearance is only relieved by the often complex network of steep-sided creeks. The vegetation is seldom more than 60 cm high, and, where grazed, often extremely short; it becomes increasingly sparse towards its lower limits.

The plants that grow on salt marshes are able to tolerate the often high salt concentrations of the soil and are known as halophytes. Many can withstand frequent submergence by the tides and even partial burial in mud or sand brought in with the sea-water. Soil salinity can vary considerably. It is generally low in estuaries, in areas of high rainfall, and fringing the tideless brackish waters of the Baltic Sea, and highest where the salt in the soil is concentrated by evaporation of water from the marsh surface during dry weather. It may also fluctuate wildly at any one site throughout the year.

The variation in salinity and climate, together with variation in the types of sediment and degree of tidal influence, produce a variety of salt-marsh habitats—a variety which is reflected in a wide range of plants and plant communities. Despite this variety, coastal salt marshes throughout Europe have certain features in common. They often show some form of zonation parallel to the shore, and, although there are no hard and fast rules, each zone usually has its own characteristic association of species.

Sea lavender (*Limonium vulgare*) has special mechanisms which enable it to deal with a salty environment. Glands on the edges of the leaves actually secrete salt so that it does not build up in the plant tissues. Flowering period: July–October.

123

Salt-marsh zones

It is usually possible to recognize at least three zones: pioneer, low marsh and high marsh. The pioneer zone is a sparsely vegetated area of mud or sand-mud that is being colonized by plants and usually occurs below the mean high water spring tides. The low marsh has a more or less complete vegetation cover and extends up the marsh to about the level of the mean high water spring tides, while the high marsh is that part between the mean and extreme high water spring tides. These three zones, however, often merge imperceptibly into one another, the transition being marked only by a gradual change in the abundance of particular species. In many cases, the zones represent a succession in time with one group of plants replacing another as the salt marsh develops. This process is a highly dynamic one and is influenced by a whole complex of environmental factors, the most important of which relate to the amount of tidal submergence.

On sheltered muddy shores, the incoming tide carries suspended particles of sediment, some of which are deposited on the surface, gradually raising its level. As the level rises, the frequency and duration of tidal submergence decreases and the level of the water-table and the aeration, salinity and drainage properties of the soil change. The plants themselves play an important part. They slow down tidal currents, enabling more sediment to be deposited and less to be eroded from the surface. They improve the physical structure of the soil, and, as they decay, increase the amounts of soil nutrients and organic matter. In addition, blue-green algae are able to fix atmospheric nitrogen, improving the initially low nutrient status of the soil. In fact, paradoxically, the plants of any given zone pave the way for their own destruction.

Although many halophytes will grow reasonably well in ordinary garden soils, their specialization for the intertidal habitat generally makes them unable to compete successfully with inland plants in less extreme conditions. Each species, therefore, tends to occupy a distinct range along the gradient from pioneer to high marsh, the lower limit being determined by the extent of a plant's adaptation to tidal submergence and the upper limit by its ability to compete with other species beginning to establish themselves in the less harsh conditions. The characteristic zones are produced by a combination of the different, frequently overlapping, ranges of the individual species. In addition to geographical variation, the species in any one zone vary with tidal range, salinity, sediment type and management—as, for example, whether or not the marsh is grazed. As happens in the case of plants on maritime cliffs or the seaweeds on rocky shores, the zonation represents a static display of the ecological lifestyles of the various plants but with the difference that, on salt

marshes, the absolute position of the zones changes with time as one group of plants is inevitably displaced by another.

THE PIONEER ZONE

Although they may play only a very small part in the development of the salt marsh, mention must be made of the 'seagrass' communities. These curious marine plants with long grass-like leaves, form extensive meadows in suitable areas all around the coast. The two commonest are the eelgrasses, *Zostera marina* and *Z. noltii*. Despite their common name they are not, strictly speaking, grasses. In the brackish waters of the Baltic Sea, *Z. noltii* is found permanently submerged but on Atlantic and North Sea coasts it occurs above the low-tide mark. *Z. marina* is found lower down the shore and, because it is more susceptible to frost, behaves as a summer annual from the French coast of the Channel northwards. The two plants are an important winter food of the Brent goose *(Branta bernicla)* and a disease which destroyed most of the Atlantic *Zostera* meadows in the early 1930s is thought to have been the cause of a serious reduction in the numbers of these birds. In the less saline waters of estuaries, in the Baltic Sea and in the brackish fjords of Denmark, other closely related flowering plants are found in *Zostera* meadows. These include the tasselweed *Ruppia maritima*, horned pondweed

In autumn, sea-blite (*Suaeda maritima*) plants turn from green into a range of reddish-purple shades. Flowering period: August–October.

Above, left: The annual glassworts (*Salicornia europaea*) form a group of very closely related species, all with swollen, succulent stems. Flowering period: August–September.

Left: The entire life cycle of the eelgrasses (*Zostera* species) takes place in water and they are often only exposed at very low water. Flowering period: June–November.

A grazed marsh, showing the darker green of the salt-marsh grass *Puccinellia maritima* with the lighter green of red fescue (*Festuca rubra*).

(*Zannichellia palustris*) and the pondweed *Potamogeton pectinatus*. More frequent, however, are seaweeds such as *Enteromorpha* species, *Ulva lactuca*, *Chaetomorpha linum* and *Porphyra umbilicalis*. These and other seaweeds, such as the *Fucus* species, *Ascophyllum nodosum* and *Bostrychia scorpioides*, extend up to the true salt-marsh pioneer zone and beyond.

The first true pioneers of the salt marsh are the annual glassworts. The various species of this small, succulent, leafless plant are collectively known as *Salicornia europaea*. Able to withstand daily submergence by sea-water, they are highly specialized, being little more than jointed stem-segments with scale-like leaf bases and no proper leaves. Because they are annuals, they also largely avoid the rigours of the strong tides and unstable mudflats: germination, growth and flowering take place mainly between the high tides of the spring and autumn equinoxes. The tides in the spring dislodge many early seedlings but, like the autumn tides, they also disperse the seeds over a wide area. The seeds of one species, encased in the fruiting head, are known to be capable of floating for up to three months in seawater before germinating. Often thinly scattered over the mud nearest the sea, glassworts may produce dense swards less than 10cm high close to the permanent marsh. Here, and on creek banks in both the low and high marsh, their autumnal colours of yellow and red are a very attractive feature.

Annual sea-blite (*Suaeda maritima*) and, particularly in brackish areas on clay sediments, perennial sea aster (*Aster tripolium*) often occur mingled with the glassworts, especially in the upper part of the zone. The sea aster is here often the form without conspicuous pale lilac ray florets. Common saltmarsh-grass (*Puccinellia maritima*), the dominant grass of the low salt marsh, may also be present and is often the sole pioneer on the sandy, sheep- and cattle-grazed marshes of Fennoscandia, Schleswig-Holstein, the west coast of Britain, and the coasts of Ireland. In Iceland and northern Norway, it is replaced by an arctic saltmarsh-grass, *Puccinellia phryganodes*, often associated with the arctic stitchwort *Stellaria humifusa* and common scurvygrass (*Cochlearia officinalis*). From Wales and East Anglia southwards, perennial glasswort (*Arthrocnemum perenne*) a Mediterranean species, is found in pioneer and low marsh zones.

In the muddier pioneer zones from Scotland and Skallingen (Denmark) to south-west France, a remarkable perennial grass, the common cord-grass (*Spartina anglica*), has become increasingly prominent during the past century. This plant was first discovered in southern England in 1870 as a sterile hybrid between the native European *Spartina maritima* and the introduced American *Spartina alterniflora*. Natural doubling of the chromosome number restored its

Right: The sea plantain (*Plantago maritima*) has a rosette of long, narrow, fleshy leaves with a tall flowering stem ending in a spike of flowers. The petals are small and brownish, about 3mm across; the yellow anthers on their long filaments are the flower's most conspicuous parts. The plants are wind-pollinated. Flowering period: June-August.

The golden samphire (*Inula crithmoides*) has two very distinct habitats. One is the high marsh zone of salt marshes, the other is the rock crevice zone on calcareous sea cliffs. The plant is easy to identify: its fleshy stems are fairly densely covered by leaves with a three-toothed tip and have several yellow flower heads at the top. Flowering period: July-August.

fertility and enabled this vigorous, mud-binding plant to spread by seed. It has extensive creeping rhizomes, firmly anchored roots, and dense, erect stems capable of growing 10 to 15cm a year through accreting mud. The plant is able to tolerate high salinities and long periods of continuous tidal submergence. Although it has had a rapid natural spread in Europe, it has also been extensively planted, with varying degrees of success, to stabilize mudflats all around the world. In the most suitable areas of north-west Europe it has formed vast meadows that exclude all other plants, often replacing the native *Spartina maritima*.

In less saline areas, particularly in the upper reaches of estuaries, a number of other plants normally found in the low or even high marsh zones of coastal marshes may act as pioneers. These include sea aster, creeping bent (*Agrostis stolonifera*), sea arrowgrass (*Triglochin maritima*) and even a species of orache, *Atriplex prostrata*, more usually found on strandlines. The most widespread of the brackish-water pioneers, however, are the sedge-like *Scirpus maritimus* and, in less saline areas, the common reed (*Phragmites australis*). Pioneer *Scirpus* meadows occur in estuaries and polders locally from western Norway and the British Isles southwards to Brittany, and on open coasts around the Baltic.

THE LOW MARSH ZONE

The two most characteristic plants of the low marsh are common saltmarsh-grass and, usually at a higher level, sea-purslane (*Halimione portulacoides*). Both sometimes cover very large areas. In the Wash on the east coast of England, for example, around 2,500ha, more than half of the total salt-marsh area, are dominated by one or both of these species. Sea-purslane, a low woody shrub with attractive grey-green leaves, reaches its northern limits in eastern Ireland, southernmost Scotland and in Denmark. It tends to be found on better-drained sites such as the edges of creeks, but where marshes are grazed, it is eliminated and common saltmarsh-grass takes over.

Typical low-marsh plants include sea arrowgrass, annual sea-blite, sea aster, sea plantain (*Plantago maritima*) and the sea-spurrey *Spergularia media*. Towards the upper edge of the zone, sea-lavender (*Limonium vulgare* and locally *L. humile*) often provides a carpet of purple flowers during early summer. In late winter and early spring the drabness of the low marsh may be relieved by splashes of white, the flowers of scurvy grass (*Cochlearia* species).

Plants occurring in the marshes of the far north include the saltmarsh-grass *Puccinellia distans* subsp. *borealis*, and the sedges *Carex salina*, *C. halophila* and *C. subspathacea*. By contrast, golden samphire (*Inula crithmoides*) which often

Sea-purslane (*Halimione portulacoides*) is a small salt marsh shrub, especially found fringing pools and channels. It grows up to about 80cms tall and is easily identified by its elliptic, mealy grey-green leaves. Flowering period: July-September.

The sea-spurrey *Spergularia marina* has flowers which are usually deep pink, about 7mm across, with the petals shorter than the sepals. Though best developed in open muddy areas, it can be found almost anywhere in the high marsh zone. Flowering period: June-August.

Salt marshes are at their best in late summer when plants such as the sea-lavender *Limonium vulgare* are in flower. Here it is growing on the edge of a muddy salt pan with cord-grass (*Spartina* species) and sea-purslane (*Halimione portulacoides*).

extends down to the higher parts of the pioneer zone, occurs from south-east England southwards and is essentially a Mediterranean species. Interestingly, the golden samphire, with its striking yellow, daisy-like heads, can be found in very different habitats in southern Britain and France, occurring on salt marshes, shingle spits and on sea cliffs.

As with the pioneer zone, certain plants found in the higher parts of coastal marshes descend into the low marsh zone in estuarine and brackish water areas. These include thrift (*Armeria maritima*), sea-milkwort *(Glaux maritima)* and sea-wormwood (*Artemisia maritima*).

The low marsh zone usually has a highly developed drainage system of creeks. Their edges are usually raised slightly higher than the intervening areas which therefore tend to drain less rapidly, and in some places semi-permanent pools, called pans, are left. Drainage may also be by hidden channels, the collapse of which can produce new pans.

THE HIGH MARSH ZONE

In contrast to the relatively few species occurring in the pioneer and low marsh zones, the high marsh, roughly between the level of mean and extreme high water spring tides, has a much greater variety. Not only are more plants capable of tolerating the smaller amount of tidal submergence, but there is also a wider range of habitats. This is because differences in soil, drainage and sedimentation become very important from one marsh to the next and even on the same marsh; there are, in addition, transitions to other coastal habitats such as sand-dune, shingle, seawalls and maritime grassland. Consequently, fewer areas are dominated by just one or two plant species and some may be very rich in species.

Particularly rich are those ungrazed communities where grasses are relatively scarce. Usually characterized by the presence of thrift, such areas may contain not only sea-lavender, sea plantain, sea arrowgrass, annual sea-blite, sea aster, sea-milkwort, sea-purslane, glasswort, sea wormwood, scurvy grass and the sea-spurrey *Spergularia media*, but, in addition, plants such as the saltmarsh rush *Juncus gerardii* and another sea-spurrey, *S. marina*. The glassworts include some species not found in the lower zones. Though these marshes occur throughout north-west Europe, the richest are probably those of East Anglia. Here, where salt marshes merge into dune and shingle, are plants such as sea pearlwort (*Sagina maritima*), buck's-horn plantain (*Plantago coronopus*), the sea-lavenders *Limonium binervosum* and *L. bellidifolium*, and sea-heath (*Frankenia laevis*). The last two are Mediterranean species at their northern limits. *Limonium binervosum* is typically a plant of maritime cliffs from western France and Britain northwards to southernmost Scotland.

Grasses do occur in the species-rich marshes, notably red fescue (*Festuca rubra*) and, in the less saline areas, creeping bent, but they only really become dominant in grazed marshes. Here, heavy grazing by sheep can produce extensive lawns of short, dense turf less than 3 cm high. Thrift, sea milkwort, buck's-horn plantain and *Juncus gerardi* may also be found in these grazed marshes. Swards dominated by fescue and bent, especially on relatively sandy soils, are locally cut for turf, which may be used, as in the west of Britain, to provide high-quality sports turf or, traditionally on the German, Danish and Dutch coasts, to cover the seaward faces of reclamation banks. The bare areas left by turf-cutting may be colonized by a variety of plants including, in the sandier and higher parts, silverweed (*Potentilla anserina*) and the centauries *Centaurium pulchellum* and *C. littorale*. Other grasses which may occur in the high marsh include both those with a wide inland distribution, such as tall fescue (*Festuca arundinacea*) and marsh foxtail (*Alopecurus geniculatus*), and others which are confined to maritime habitats such as the foxtail *A. bulbosus* and *Parapholis strigosa*. Of the last two, the foxtail is rather uncommon, occurring locally from England and the Netherlands southwards. *Parapholis strigosa* is a rather curious-looking grass which can easily be overlooked in dense grassland. Only when the creamy-white anthers are

visible does it become obvious that the stiff, slender leaf-like structures are the flowering spikes of a grass. Its more Mediterranean relative, *P. incurva*, extends north to the southern and eastern coasts of England and south Wales.

One grass which can become dominant in the high marsh, particularly on silty, ungrazed marshes, is sea couch-grass (*Elymus pycnanthus*). This coarse, unpalatable plant, absent from Fennoscandia, Scotland and the northern part of Ireland, may also be found on stable dunes, shingle, the seaward faces of seawalls, reclaimed land and along the banks of tidal rivers. It forms hybrids with the sand-dune couch-grass *E. farctus* and the widespread common couch-grass (*E. repens*). Common couch-grass largely replaces sea couch-grass in suitable habitats in northern Britain, Iceland and Fennoscandia.

The high marsh also features a number of rushes and sedges. Two rushes found throughout Europe and locally dominant are *Juncus gerardii* and *J. maritimus*. *J. gerardii* is a very variable plant which can be found mingling with other species in short turf, but the tall spreading tufts of *J. maritimus* tend to eliminate everything else. Further up the marsh and usually colonizing bare mud are the toad rush (*J. bufonius*) and, in brackish swamps, *J. articulatus*. Another rush which occurs in brackish marshes and in damp hollows between sand-dunes is *J. acutus*, which forms tall, dense

Sea-arrowgrass (*Triglochin maritima*) could easily be confused with the sea plantain, but its leaves sheath the base of the stem and the flowering spike is not so dense, so that individual flower stalks and the elongated fruit are clearly visible. Flowering period: July-September.

Right: The sea-milkwort (*Glaux maritima*) is a member of the primrose family. It is succulent with fleshy, creeping stems and small, simple leaves. The flowers, borne in the axils of the leaves, have no petals, but the sepals are pink. The plant is very common in the high marsh zone. Flowering period: June-August.

Right: Silverweed (*Potentilla anserina*) often colonizes bare areas of marsh where turf-cutting has removed the vegetation. The individual rosettes of silky, silvery leaves are connected by long red stolons and they bear the solitary yellow flowers on long stalks. Flowering period: June-August.

129

tussocks of stiff, formidable, sharp-pointed stems. This is a Mediterranean species which extends northwards to southern Ireland. The sedges *Carex extensa*, *C. distans* and, less commonly, *C. punctata* occur locally northwards to about 60°N in Fennoscandia. On the other hand, *Carex recta*, *C. paleacea*, *C. mackenziei* and *C. glareosa* are more northerly, growing in the brackish marshes of Fennoscandia and, in the case of the last two, in Iceland. *Carex divisa* is a plant of maritime grasslands and estuaries from Scotland and Belgium southwards.

Other sedge-like plants of the high marsh are *Scirpus maritimus* and *Blysmus rufus*; both are more common in northern and brackish areas, sometimes forming virtually pure swards. *Blysmus* is particularly common on the Swedish and German coasts of the Baltic and the Gulf of Bothnia.

Brackish marshes and strandlines

Although they may grow below the level of the highest spring tides, many plants of the high marsh are more common higher up in areas reached only by occasional storm tides, perhaps once in three or four years. A great variety of plants may be found in such areas, many of them not strictly halophytes, being widely distributed inland on non-saline soils. They include the common reed, white clover (*Trifolium repens*), autumn hawkbit (*Leontodon autumnalis*), broad-leaved dock (*Rumex obtusifolius*), marsh arrowgrass (*Triglochin palustris*), bittersweet (*Solanum dulcamara*), the sedge *Carex otrubae*, tufted hair-grass (*Deschampsia cespitosa*), meadowsweet (*Filipendula ulmaria*) and yellow iris (*Iris pseudacorus*). On the west coasts of Ireland and Scotland the distinctive flowers of these last two species may even be seen in the wetter areas of the high marsh with, nearby, thrift, red fescue and non-halophytes such as creeping thistle (*Cirsium arvense*) and even a moorland species, purple moor-grass (*Molinia caerulea*). The descent of these plants, and of a number of mosses, into the high marsh may be possible because high rainfall and low evaporation keep salinity low.

Two plants largely confined to the higher marsh are the clover *Trifolium squamosum* and the grass *Polypogon monspeliensis*; both are species of southern Europe which just reach the coast of southern England. Other plants which become progressively rarer and coastal towards the north, are slender hare's-ear (*Bupleurum tenuissimum*), marsh-mallow (*Althaea officinalis*) and strawberry clover (*Trifolium fragiferum*). Several occur in both inland and upper coastal marshes, but are generally more common at the coast. These include wild celery (*Apium graveolens*), the clubrush *Scirpus lacustris* subsp. *tabernaemontani*, brookweed (*Samolus valerandi*) and, particularly in the north of its range, the

The orache *Atriplex prostata* is particularly characteristic of strandlines where plant and algal debris are deposited, and grows rapidly where there is a high nutrient content. The inconspicuous flowers are clustered in the axils of the leaves, high on the stems. Flowering period: July-September.

Right: Salsify (*Tragopogon porrifolius*) has been introduced into the region and is widely cultivated for its edible root. It has escaped from cultivation and can be found in some grasslands, including reclaimed marshlands. Flowering period: June-August.

water-dropwort *Oenanthe lachenalii*. Of the spike rushes (*Eleocharis*), *E. parvula* is almost entirely coastal, *E. uniglumis* is more frequent on coastal marshes, while *E. palustris* and *E. quinqueflora* are inland marsh species which may descend to the brackish zones.

A complete list of the plants to be found in European brackish marshes would be a very long one and it would even have to include several plants from the lower zones. Of these, sea plantain, sea aster and common saltmarsh-grass, for example, each make up a number of almost separate populations consisting of plants genetically adapted to the environmental conditions prevailing at a particular level on the marsh. The list would also include plants more usually associated with strandlines and others more frequently found nowadays on reclaimed land.

A number of plants are characteristic of areas where plant and other debris have been washed ashore by the highest tides and either deposited as a drift line or become mixed with sediment. They may grow here because their seeds have been washed up with the tidal drift and this is the absolute limit of tidal submergence, or because they benefit from the extra nitrogen provided by the rotting organic debris. Certainly plants of annual sea-blite, various species of orache, for example *Atriplex prostrata* and *A. littoralis*, and curled dock (*Rumex crispus*) growing on the strandline are often taller and

130

seventeenth century. The habitats within reclaimed land include seawalls and earth embankments, open muddy saline areas where vehicles or cattle constantly disturb the ground, grassland, grazed marshes, reed swamp and drainage ditches.

These habitats are often rich in species, many of which are not halophytes. Some, such as the thistle *Carduus tenuifolius*, salsify *(Tragopogon porrifolius)* and meadow barley *(Hordeum secalinum)* are becoming increasingly restricted to reclaimed land as their inland habitats disappear under cultivation. Others are naturally more characteristic of reclaimed land. These include annual grasses such as sea barley *(Hordeum marinum)* and several species of saltmarsh-grass, *Puccinellia distans, P. rupestris* and *P. fasciculata*, which seem to require constantly disturbed, often highly saline, muddy ground. *P. fasciculata*, for example, spread dramatically around the Dutch coast following the extensive construction of seawalls after the 1953 floods. Other plants of reclaimed land include the small goosefoot *Chenopodium botryodes* on mud, the umbellifer *Peucedanum officinale* on grassy banks, and the grass-like tasselweed *Ruppia cirrhosa* and water-crowfoot *Ranunculus baudotii* in pools and ditches. Reclaimed land is also often the best place to look for many plants of high marsh and brackish fen areas such as sea-spurrey and sea beet.

Major salt marsh types

Despite their variety, and the complications introduced by grazing and land reclamation, it is possible to recognize groups of similar salt marshes in north-west Europe. One major group is grass-dominated, usually sandy, often grazed and found mainly in Fennoscandia and western parts of the British Isles. Another includes those marshes usually found on finer sediments and with a wide range of plant communities including some essentially Mediterranean species. Rarely grazed, marshes of this type are well developed around the southern part of the North Sea and extend along both sides of the English Channel. Two further groups are the brackish Baltic marshes and the subarctic marshes of northern Fennoscandia and Iceland. Other types, for example in north-west Scotland, in south-west Ireland (where the marsh soils are very peaty) and in the English Channel, have been recognized on the basis of differences in climate, physical structure, or the plants found there. Salt marshes also occur on saline areas well inland.

Although they may lack the spectacular scenery of maritime cliffs, the pleasant dryness of sand-dunes, or the rich variety of species on chalk grassland, salt marshes are nevertheless fascinating areas to look for interesting and often attractive plants. Familiarity with them serves to enhance their singular appeal.

more vigorous than their counterparts on the tidal marsh. Other characteristic plants of the strandline are sea couch-grass, scentless mayweed *(Matricaria maritima)*, dittander *(Lepidium latifolium)*, sea beet *(Beta vulgaris* subsp. *maritima)*, the related *Bassia hirsuta*, and the crucifer *Erysimum hieracifolium*, the last two having rather patchy distributions along the European coast. Where salt marsh adjoins sand-dune and shingle, strandline plants such as sea rocket *(Cakile maritima)* and the shrubby sea-blite *Suaeda vera* may occur.

Reclaimed land

A number of coastal plants are nowadays found mostly on land reclaimed from the sea. This is particularly extensive along the Dutch, north-west German, Danish and south-east English coasts. For example, over 32,000 ha have been reclaimed around the Wash since the beginning of the

10
Sand-dunes and shingle beaches

Sand-dunes

The formation of sand-dunes requires a continuous supply of mobile sand and a strong prevailing wind. In north-west Europe the best-developed dune systems are formed in coastal areas, although vast inland dunes occur elsewhere, particularly in arid regions. Sand for coastal dunes usually comes from a gently sloping sandy shore, where flats are exposed at low tide, or it may be derived from offshore sandbanks and bars similarly exposed. In north-west Europe prevailing onshore winds encourage dune building on the Atlantic, North Sea and English Channel coasts.

Dune formation is essentially a physical process. When the wind is strong enough and the sand sufficiently dry, the grains are blown into the air. On falling, they often set other grains in motion and may themselves become airborne again; this process is called saltation. The wind can also cause the surface sand to creep bodily forwards. The sand will continue to move until it meets an obstruction. This may be only a slight irregularity of the surface but it will probably be sufficient to allow the heavier grains to settle on the calmer, leeward side. The result of this process is the development, usually at right-angles to the wind, of a dune with a steep windward and gentler leeward slope. As sand continues to move up the windward side and over the top, the crest moves landwards, and new dunes form on the seaward side. Such mobile, advancing dunes, mainly free of vegetation, occur in many parts of the world but are largely absent from north-west Europe where, from an early stage, dune formation is strongly influenced by colonizing vegetation. This has the effect of stabilizing the dunes, preventing their landward march and generally softening and lowering their natural contours. The lines of dunes that extend inland parallel to the coast in so many dune systems have largely been formed *in situ*, the youngest being nearest the sea. At least in some places, it is not the dunes that are advancing inland but the

Marram grass (*Ammophila arenaria*) is one of the early colonists of developing sand-dunes, where it encourages further sand deposition by slowing down the wind near the sand surface. Flowering period: July–August.

coast which is extending seawards. In north-west Europe most of the dune systems appear to have developed during the last thousand years, but the formation of new dunes appears now to be less active.

STRANDLINES AND FOREDUNES

At the seaward edge of most dune systems there is a characteristic strandline plant community that marks the limit of the highest spring tides. It is dominated by annual species such as the spiny, succulent saltwort *(Salsola kali)*, and the crucifer, sea rocket *(Cakile maritima)*, together with several species of orache *(Atriplex)*, notably *A. littoralis*, *A. glabriuscula*, *A. prostrata* and *A. laciniata*. The Atlantic knotgrass *Polygonum oxyspermum* subsp. *raii* may also be present in this community on shores from north-west France to southern Norway and *P. maritimum* from northern France southwards. Seeds of these annual halophytes germinate among nutrient-rich debris and decaying seaweed, establishing deep and complex root systems. Strandline vegetation is often only partially developed on dune systems and rarely produces a closed community. It may also vary markedly from year to year in both its extent and composition.

The strandline itself provides a natural, if small, barrier obstructing the movement of wind-borne sand grains and this is accentuated by the colonizing plants. In this way embryo foredunes may form around the strandline plants, but they remain small and isolated. They are generally blown away when the plants die in autumn, but may provide a niche for the establishment of the perennial grasses, sand couch *(Elymus farctus)* and lyme-grass *(Leymus arenarius)*, which also colonize just above the strandline. Both species are widely distributed along the shores of north-west Europe, although lyme-grass is rather more northerly in its range. Both are perennials and have long-lived rhizomes. They are therefore far more effective than the strandline plants in stabilizing sand and, because they continually grow upward through fresh sand, in increasing the size of the dune. The plants of these embryo dunes are salt-tolerant, being able to withstand the effects of sea spray and even occasional inundation by sea water. Another perennial, the creeping sea sandwort *(Honkenya peploides)* sometimes grows in the strandline community and its cushions may similarly act as a focus for dune formation.

In time, the embryo dunes tend to merge, producing foredunes dominated by sand couch. This plant may establish itself from seed or from broken fragments of rhizomes. At first it grows by means of short, horizontal rhizomes from which grow aerial shoots, but later the plant produces longer, spreading rhizomes which increase the potential for further foredune building. Sand couch

On sandy shores, the most characteristic flower of the strandline is the sea rocket *(Cakile maritima)* which may form a line of lilac-flowered plants marking the driftline. Behind it here are young marram *(Ammophila arenaria)* dunes. Flowering period: June-August.

Lyme-grass *(Leymus arenarius)* is a common grass of foredunes in more northern areas. It is much broader-leaved than marram *(Ammophila arenaria)* but not as effective at dune building. Flowering period: July-August.

The sea sandwort (*Honkenya peploides*) is a perennial, growing at the strandline and rather further inland. Its fleshy-leaved shoots trap sand and form fairly dense hummocks. The greenish-white flowers are not very obvious. Flowering period: May-August.

In actively growing or mobile dunes, there are large areas of bare sand, often rippled by the wind. Marram (*Ammophila arenaria*) grows vigorously and in the lee of its tussocks, where windspeed is reduced, sand is deposited, so building up the dunes.

foredunes remain small, reaching a height of only 1-2m. They are generally developed directly behind the annual strandline community, but frequently the separation is not very sharp.

ACTIVELY GROWING DUNES

The effect of sand couch and other plants is to raise the foredunes and so reduce the chances of flooding by sea water, even at the highest of spring tides. These drier, less saline conditions permit the main dune-building grass, marram (*Ammophila arenaria*) to colonize and to replace the foredune grasses. Marram is a robust, rhizomatous grass, well-adapted to growth in mobile, often extremely dry sand. The lower surface of the tough grey-green leaves is thickly covered with cutin, and stomata (the epidermal pores) are confined to the upper surface. In dry weather the leaves curl inwards, thus restricting water loss. Marram will grow vigorously and keep pace with up to about 40cm per year of sand deposition; it can even tolerate rates as high as 100cm per year. The shoots of marram are longer and more erect than those of sand couch and so they are more efficient at

Amongst the marram on actively-growing dunes the very spiny sea holly (*Eryngium maritimum*) can be found. The whole plant is bluish green, though the flowers within the head are lilac. Growing with the sea holly is the sea spurge (*Euphorbia paralias*). Flowering period: July–August.

Right: Hound's-tongue (*Cynoglossum officinale*) is a grey-leaved, silky-haired biennial which grows in dry places, particularly near the sea. It has red-purple flowers and, later, four flattened oval nutlets, covered by short, barbed spines. The plant smells of mice. Flowering period: June–August.

trapping sand. Like sand couch, marram may establish itself from seed or from fragments of rhizomes, similarly producing horizontal rhizomes from which vertical shoots grow. When a vertical, leafy shoot becomes covered by sand, new axillary shoots develop which eventually reach the surface. This process continues and ultimately a tussock may develop. Provided the sand is moist, adventitious roots form on the vertical shoots just below the surface. The old rhizomes joining the deeper, horizontal rhizomes ultimately break down, but only after many years. Marram shows an exceptional capacity for regrowth under conditions of constant sand deposition and can build up lofty mobile dunes that are often more than 20m high. Lyme-grass commonly grows with marram on European dunes from the Netherlands northwards. Sometimes it may dominate a distinct zone on the seaward side of the marram, but more frequently it is present only in isolated clumps. It is less effective than marram at dune building, and so has not been widely used for dune stabilization.

FIRST STAGES OF DUNE STABILIZATION
In the most actively growing areas of these dunes, marram and lyme-grass may be the only plants. There is always much bare sand between the isolated grass shoots and tussocks; consequently, where sand is deposited at a slower rate,

scattered individuals of other plants may appear. A subspecies of red fescue (*Festuca rubra* subsp. *arenaria*) is probably the most important ecologically but other early colonists include maritime species such as sea spurge (*Euphorbia paralias*), Portland spurge (*E. portlandica*), sea-holly (*Eryngium maritimum*), sea bindweed (*Calystegia soldanella*), and sea sandwort. The association of marram and sea spurge replaces that of marram and lyme-grass along the Atlantic coasts south and west of the Netherlands. Portland spurge has a similar but more restricted distribution to that of sea spurge, reaching its easterly limit on the coast of Manche, in north-west France. Sea-holly, a Mediterranean species, is widespread around the Atlantic and North Sea coasts northwards to southern Scandinavia and the Baltic Sea. Two other Mediterranean species, the stock *Matthiola sinuata* and the composite *Otanthus maritimus* extend as far north as Brittany, south-west England and southern Ireland. Non-maritime 'weedy' species may be well represented in the open marram community; these include hound's tongue (*Cynoglossum officinale*), ragwort (*Senecio jacobaea*), groundsel (*S. vulgaris*), creeping thistle (*Cirsium arvense*), spear thistle (*C. vulgare*) and coltsfoot (*Tussilago farfara*). Some, such as scarlet pimpernel (*Anagallis arvensis*), are common weeds of arable fields.

Whereas marram is the main dune builder, the other early

Amongst the early colonists of stabilizing dunes are the sea bindweed *(Calystegia soldanella)* (left) and dune pansies *(Viola tricolor* subsp. *curtisii)* (below, left). Flowering periods: June-August and April-September.

Below: Several weedy plants are found in dunes once the surface begins to stabilize. Here the marram has been invaded by yellow ragwort *(Senecio jacobaea)* and rosebay willowherb *(Epilobium angustifolium)*. Flowering period: June-October.

colonists, particularly red fescue, help to stabilize the surface. Many of these plants have a basal rosette of leaves around which sand may accumulate; others spread rapidly through or over the surface sand by rhizomes or runners. The sand sedge *(Carex arenaria)* produces a long, unbranched rhizome, throwing up a shoot at approximately every fourth node; it may also be an early colonist of bare areas of open sand. Another group of plants, the winter annuals, are often conspicuous early in the year. Seeds of these dune annuals, such as the small mouse-ear *Cerastium semidecandrum*, common whitlowgrass *(Erophila verna)*, the forget-me-not *Myosotis ramosissima* and the grass *Phleum arenarium*, germinate in the autumn when the sand is moist. The seedlings overwinter and grow vigorously in the spring, flowering and fruiting well before the summer drought. It is important to realize that, because of the rapid drainage on the sand dunes, normal summer weather can very quickly result in surface drought. The same group of winter annuals is also typical of disturbed sand in more stable dune areas. Often growing with them is the perennial pansy *Viola tricolor* subsp. *curtisii*, its flowers ranging in colour from pure yellow to blue-violet. It is common on dune systems along the western coasts of the British Isles, the French Channel coast and the shores of the southern North Sea and the Baltic Sea.

Despite their instability, active dunes may eventually be colonized by a wide range of species. These vary considerably from place to place, depending for example, on the abundance of potential colonizing plants in inland areas immediately adjacent to the dunes, and also on their powers of dispersal. Another factor is the chemical nature of the sand itself. Active dunes are often described as yellow or white dunes, according to the relative proportions of yellow, iron oxide-stained sand and fragmented, white, calcium-rich shell material. Yellow dunes, with little shell material, are relatively acid and the number of potential colonizing species is limited. On the other hand, as the proportion of shell fragments increases, the variety of colonizing species is considerably increased and includes a number of pronounced calcicole plants.

LATER STAGES OF STABILIZATION

With increasing distance inland, the rate at which sand is deposited slows down. Although marram is still abundant, it gradually loses its dominance as an increasing number of species are able to enter the community.

Mosses are perhaps the most obvious new colonists and these also help to stabilize the sand, usually appearing at first on the leeward side of the dune crests, often in surface depressions. *Bryum pendulum* and *Ceratodon purpureus* are frequent pioneers, followed by *Tortula ruraliformis*, a moss

Ephedra distachya is not unlike broom in general form, but is in fact a gymnosperm, more closely related to pines than to flowering plants. It has very inconspicuous flowers, but bright pink 'fruits'. It is restricted to the dunes in the south of the region.

The sand of the dunes is usually very low in essential nutrients. Plants of the pea family, such as the common bird's-foot-trefoil (*Lotus corniculatus*) have nodules on their roots in which live nitrogen-fixing bacteria. This makes the plants less dependent on fixed nitrogen from the soil, giving them an advantage in such situations. Flowering period: June-September.

with remarkable powers of recovery from desiccation. Most mosses of the white and yellow dunes even show some ability to grow and regenerate in places where some sand is still accumulating. These pioneer tuft-forming species are followed by others with a more spreading or mat-forming habit, such as *Brachythecium albicans* and *Camptothecium lutescens*.

The tufted grass *Corynephorus canescens* is an important colonist of acid sand-dunes. It is a suboceanic species extending from southern Scandinavia to the Iberian peninsula, reaching East Anglia at its north-westerly limit. When buried by sand it responds in the same way as marram and, where abundant, may play a major stabilizing role, but it can tolerate only moderate sand deposition.

As the dunes become more stable, they become completely covered with vegetation; only where there has been local disturbance can bare sand be seen. Under these conditions, marram loses its vigour and only moribund shoots remain which seldom flower. The precise reason for this decline is not known but the most likely explanation is that as less and less sand is deposited, marram is unable to develop new shoots and continue adventitious root production. With its decline, other grasses, notably red fescue and the meadow-grass *Poa pratensis* subsp. *subcaerulea*, increase in abundance, accompanied by sand sedge and legumes such as

common bird's-foot-trefoil (*Lotus corniculatus*), common restharrow (*Ononis repens*) and white clover (*Trifolium repens*). The legumes are able to fix atmospheric nitrogen by means of the bacteria in their root nodules and so they are less affected than other plants by the inherent nitrogen deficiency of the sandy soil.

The species composition of these 'fixed' dunes varies greatly but generally those developed on calcareous sand have the richest flora, somewhat similar to that of limestone grassland. Such areas are extremely colourful in the flowering season, typically a mixture of yellow flowers such as those of bird's-foot-trefoil, lady's-bedstraw (*Galium verum*), mouse-ear hawkweed (*Hieracium pilosella*), a dune variety of the lesser meadow-rue (*Thalictrum minus*), species of evening-primrose (*Oenothera*), yellow-wort (*Blackstonia perfoliata*) and biting stonecrop (*Sedum acre*); of pink flowers such as common restharrow and species of centaury (*Centaurium*); and of purple flowers, such as wild thyme (*Thymus praecox*) and viper's-bugloss (*Echium vulgare*).

A feature of the later stages of stabilization is an abundance of mat-forming mosses and lichens, the latter mainly species of *Cladonia* and *Peltigera*. Because of the dominant grey-green colour of the vegetation at this stage, these 'fixed' dunes are often referred to as grey dunes.

An interesting variant of the succession from yellow to

Left: The Jersey pink (*Dianthus gallicus*) is found in the south of the region, from Brittany and Jersey southwards, in the moderately stable vegetation of the grey dunes. Flowering period: June-August.

The marsh helleborine (*Epipactis palustris*) is one of the most characteristic plants of damp dune slacks. It is a late flowering orchid, the only one still commonly found in the dunes. Here it is growing surrounded by the creeping willow (*Salix repens*). Flowering period: June-August.

grey dunes can occur on the Atlantic coast of France where, after initial colonization by mosses, the composite *Helichrysum stoechas* invades followed later on by the curious switch-like *Ephedra distachya* subsp. *distachya* and a range of lichens. The pink *Dianthus gallicus* may be present in this community at a later stage when grey dunes give way to scrub. These dunes also include some Mediterranean species at their northern limits, such as the silvery haired *Medicago marina* and the lily-like *Pancratium maritimum*, as well as some only found on the Atlantic coasts of France and north-west Spain, for example the pale blue kidney vetch *Astragalus baionensis* and the toadflax *Linaria arenaria*, which has been introduced into a dune system in Britain.

FINAL STAGES OF SUCCESSION

Dune grassland represents a fairly stable stage in the succession. One particularly interesting type is known as machair and is found only on broad stretches of level, calcareous sandy soils in western and north-west Scotland. Many of the species present are typical of dune grassland, but, in addition, there is an abundance of orchids such as northern marsh-orchid (*Dactylorhiza majalis* subsp. *purpurella*), fragrant orchid (*Gymnadenia conopsea*) and dark-red helleborine (*Epipactis atrorubens*). Globeflower (*Trollius europaeus*) is sometimes frequent in wetter areas.

The extent of further changes is largely determined by the direct or indirect activities of man. Provided that grazing by rabbits or domestic animals is not too intensive, the structure of the grassland is generally maintained, but overgrazing may lead to erosion. On acidic sands, ungrazed grasslands can give way to heathland with heather (*Calluna vulgaris*) and other ericaceous dwarf shrubs. Bracken (*Pteridium aquilinum*) may invade and become dominant if not checked. There may even be partial development of heathland on the oldest areas of more calcareous dune grasslands, as, with time and particularly in high rainfall areas, bases are leached out of the sand. This process, together with the increase in humus, causes the soil gradually to become more acid, allowing calcifuge heathland species to appear. More often, where there is little or no grazing, dune grassland is succeeded by dune scrub, characterized by the presence of spiny shrubs such as hawthorn (*Crataegus monogyna*), species of gorse (*Ulex*), blackthorn (*Prunus spinosa*), burnet rose (*Rosa pimpinellifolia*) and species of bramble (*Rubus*), together with other shrubs and low-growing trees including elder (*Sambucus nigra*) and privet (*Ligustrum vulgare*). Sea-buckthorn (*Hippophaë rhamnoides*), the only truly maritime shrub, is abundant on dunes along the east coast of Britain and the Atlantic, North Sea and Baltic Sea coasts of mainland Europe. It is a vigorous, spiny, salt-tolerant plant which will spread rapidly by means of suckers even where the sand is mobile, to the exclusion of nearly all other species beneath it. Where grazing intensity is low it can be very difficult to control. The feathery-branched Mediterranean shrubs tamarisk (*Tamarix anglica* and *T. gallica*), found in some coastal areas in north-west France and southern England, are generally naturalized introductions.

If left undisturbed, dune scrub would give way to woodland. This rarely happens but conifers, particularly Corsican pine (*Pinus nigra*) and Scots pine (*P. sylvestris*), have been extensively planted in certain areas, as, for example, on the Culbin Sands in north-east Scotland. On more acidic soils, such as the dune systems of the Netherlands, downy birch (*Betula pubescens*) and, eventually pedunculate oak (*Quercus robur*) woodland may develop. By contrast, on the dunes along the Bay of Biscay coasts the characteristic trees are evergreen oak (*Q. ilex*) and maritime pine (*Pinus pinaster*). Only the former is native north of the Gironde estuary but both species have been extensively planted.

DUNE SLACKS

Dune slacks are areas of firm, usually moist sand lying in the hollows between lines of dunes. They have a very varied flora which is influenced by the average depth and fluctuations of the water table, the extent of further sand deposition and the salinity and shell content of the sand. Near the shore, where salinity and sand deposition are usually highest, the creeping bent (*Agrostis stolonifera*) and buck's-horn plantain (*Plantago coronopus*) may be early colonists, together with lesser hawkbit (*Leontodon taraxacoides*) and other rosette-forming species in the drier areas. Mosses, particularly species of *Bryum*, may also play an important role. Further inland, in wet slacks where water stands during the winter months, a few maritime species may still persist, such as the rushes *Juncus acutus*, *J. maritimus* and *J. balticus*, the club-rush *Scirpus maritimus*, sea-lavender (*Limonium* species) and

The burnet rose (*Rosa pimpinellifolia*) is a low-growing, very spiny rose that spreads by suckering to form small thickets on stabilized dunes. The leaves have 3 to 5 pairs of small, oval, toothed leaflets and the flowers are creamy-white, replaced later by round, purplish-black hips. Flowering period: May-July.

sea-milkwort (*Glaux maritima*). In places where the risk of flooding by sea water is negligible, wet slack vegetation may be very similar to that of inland marsh or fen. Where there are permanent pools, aquatic plants such as species of pondweed (*Potamogeton*) and shoreweed (*Littorella uniflora*) may be present. A high shell content in the sand gives rise to calcareous pools with a vegetation resembling that of rich fens, dominated by sedges and rushes together with marsh pennywort (*Hydrocotyle vulgaris*), water mint (*Mentha aquatica*), lesser spearwort (*Ranunculus flammula*), yellow iris (*Iris pseudacorus*), grass-of-Parnassus (*Parnassia palustris*), marsh helleborine (*Epipactis palustris*) and other wetland orchids. Mosses and liverworts are also well represented here. Moist slack communities often have a very rich flora and some of the species may be local or very rare, such as the coral-root (*Corallorhiza trifida*), the yellow semi-parasitic *Parentucellia viscosa* and the two diminutive members of the gentian family, *Exaculum pusillum* and the yellow-flowered *Cicendia filiformis*.

An important dune slack plant of Atlantic coasts is a subspecies of the creeping willow (*Salix repens* subsp. *argentea*). Seeds of this creeping shrub will germinate in moist sand even where salinity reaches a third of that of sea water. Where sand deposition is low, the plant spreads extensively to produce a matted carpet of upright leafy

Left: Sea buckthorn (*Hippophae rhamnoides*) is a thorny, grey-leaved shrub which can form impenetrable thickets on stabilizing dunes. It has tiny green flowers without petals, which are replaced by bright orange berries. Flowering period: April-May.

The yellow bird's-nest (*Monotropa hypopitys*) is characteristically found amongst creeping willow (*Salix repens*) in dune slacks. It contains no chlorophyll and is solely dependent for its food on matter obtained from the decomposition of the surrounding dead plants. Flowering period: June-August.

shoots, but in drier areas where deposition is higher, small dunes form around the shoots which grow up through the sand to form distinct hummocks. Particularly characteristic of the humus-rich soil beneath this prolific litter producer are the saprophytic yellow bird's-nest (*Monotropa hypopitys*) and the wintergreen *Pyrola rotundifolia* subsp. *maritima*. With time, creeping willow may be replaced by other willow species such as grey willow (*Salix cinerea*) and eared willow (*S. aurita*), by alder (*Alnus glutinosa*) and finally on more acidic dunes, by birch.

DESTRUCTION OF DUNES AND DUNE VEGETATION
Sand-dunes are fragile structures. Exceptional storminess, particularly if associated with an increase in the amount of available sand, may accelerate dune formation beyond the level that marram can tolerate. The marram may then be overwhelmed, causing the dune to become mobile and advance inland over the dune slack lying in its lee. The best example of this in north-west Europe is the Culbin Sands, in eastern Scotland, where an appreciable area of agricultural land has been buried beneath the advancing dunes.

Destruction of plant-colonized dunes may also be caused by freak storms, particularly when these come from a direction contrary to the prevailing winds. The wind may then tear apart the partial plant cover, removing quantities of

sand which then accumulate as a fan-shaped deposit in the adjacent slack. These blow-outs vary greatly in size and are most impressive in the main marram dunes where the complex rhizome and root systems are exposed. They can occur, though less commonly, in stable dunes. Burrowing by rabbits and excessive trampling by animals, including man, can also lead to substantial erosion. Blow-outs may develop into slacks if they occur close to the water-table, but elsewhere plants, particularly the sand sedge, slowly begin the process of recolonization.

Shingle beaches

Shingle beaches are not as common as sand-dunes along the coastlines of north-west Europe and, because of their very unstable nature, comparatively few are colonized to any great extent by plants. Some of the finest examples occur on the south and east coasts of England. Shingle is composed of rounded pebbles of varying size and may be derived from eroded glacial materials, from river gravels or from the sea-bed. The continuous wave action may deposit shingle in a number of ways, but the key factors are the availability of suitable material, the strength and direction of wind and waves, and the tidal range. Shingle is usually deposited as a beach with a well-marked ridge, or storm crest. Sometimes there are several crests, as when a series of shingle beaches are thrown up one in front of another, usually by onshore gales. These are called apposition beaches. Shingle beaches nearly always show movement of the shingle along their length and, particularly where the coastline changes direction, the beach may develop away from the shore as a shingle spit. Contrary wave action often deflects the tip of the spit back towards the land to form a hook. The main spit may then start growing again, only to be interrupted by further hook formation. Most shingle spits, therefore, have a terminal hook and a varying number of laterals, each of which represents a stage in the evolution of the spit. Sometimes a shingle beach may be thrown up some distance offshore as a bar running parallel to the coast. This, too, may be mobile.

Although this chapter is concerned with the vegetation of shingle beaches, spits and bars are important because they provide the sheltered conditions along their landward margins which are necessary for the development of salt marshes.

The physical nature of shingle makes it a very unsuitable habitat for the growth of most plants. Colonization depends on the presence of fine particles of sand, silt or organic matter between the pebbles. Where such material is altogether lacking, encrusting lichens may be the only colonists but where decaying seaweed (wrack) is mixed with a varying proportion of sand, the range of species may be great, depending largely on salinity and drainage. Typical foreshore plants include prostrate annuals such as species of orache, especially *Atriplex glabriuscula*, and a coastal prostrate variety of cleavers *(Galium aparine)*; and perennials, including sea-beet *(Beta vulgaris* subsp. *maritima)*, scentless mayweed *(Matricaria maritima)*, a coastal form of curled dock *(Rumex crispus)* and sea campion *(Silene vulgaris* subsp. *maritima)*. Where drainage is poor, silverweed *(Potentilla anserina)* and perennial sow-thistle *(Sonchus arvensis)* may be abundant. The oyster plant *(Mertensia maritima)* is characteristic of northern foreshores, extending from Spitsbergen southwards to northern England.

Sandy shingle beaches resemble partially fixed dunes so it is not surprising that a range of dune species may be present, such as sea sandwort, the grasses *Poa pratensis*, sand couch and the closely-related *Elymus pycnanthus* and sand sedge. Similarly, where silt is mixed with the shingle, salt-marsh species may be dominant, for example, sea-milkwort, sea wormwood *(Artemisia maritima)*, common saltmarsh-grass *(Puccinellia maritima)* and sea-purslane *(Halimione portulacoides)*, the precise species composition depending on the frequency of flooding.

Shingle beach communities can be classified according to the stability of the shingle. Where winter storms cause considerable disturbance, summer annuals such as species of

orache may be the only colonists. On beaches which remain stable for three or four years, short-lived perennials such as biting stonecrop and the distinctive yellow horned-poppy *(Glaucium flavum)* predominate, together with some annuals, notably the small grass *Desmazeria marina*. If a beach is rarely subject to disturbance but is still in the range of occasional heavy sea-spray, long-lived perennials predominate, for example sea campion, the prostrate, fleshy maritime variety of bittersweet *(Solanum dulcamara)* and sea-kale *(Crambe maritima)*. Although these are very deep-rooted species, the water table is usually below their rooting zone. Nevertheless, they are able to obtain water from percolating rain water or from dew formed on the surface of the pebbles in the top layers of the shingle.

The vegetation of shingle beaches may be distinctly zoned, the zones being related to changes in stability since few species are able to tolerate active shingle deposition. An exception is the shrubby sea-blite *Suaeda vera*. This grows to a height of about 1 m and may form a line of bushes marking the limit of the spring tides on shingle beaches from East

Left: The sea pea (*Lathyrus japonicus*), another northern shingle plant, has large, striking flowers. It scrambles over shingle, even surviving burial during stormy periods. Flowering period: June-August.

Below: The yellow horned-poppy (*Glaucium flavum*) is particularly characteristic of coastal shingle. There is no mistaking its grey-green foliage and bright yellow flowers, replaced later by a capsule which may be as long as 30cm. Flowering period: June-August.

Left: The oyster plant (*Mertensia maritima*) is commonest on northern shingle beaches, such as this beach of volcanic debris in Iceland. Flowering period: June-August.

Left: Large cabbage-like plants of sea-kale (*Crambe maritima*) form a notable feature of shingle banks, particularly when the grey-green foliage is almost hidden behind masses of white flowers. Its fruits float and are dispersed by the sea in which they can remain for many days without damage. Flowering period: June-August.

The sea campion (*Silene vulgaris* subsp. *maritima*) differs from the bladder campion (subsp. *vulgaris*) in being low growing and having larger flowers. It occurs not only in stony coastal habitats but also in the mountains. Flowering period: May-August.

Anglia and north-west France southwards. This species is very well adapted to survive in mobile shingle since its shoots react to burial in much the same way as those of marram in sand. Sea-kale, sea campion, sea sandwort and sea pea (*Lathyrus japonicus*) can all withstand occasional burial. Sea pea is a primary colonist of shingle and has a northern distribution which, in north-west Europe, extends from northern Norway and Finland to Denmark and south-west England.

On undisturbed beaches out of the range of sea-spray, as for example on the more landward apposition banks, the vegetation may become denser, eventually producing a grass-heath. False oat-grass (*Arrhenatherum elatius*), red fescue, herb-robert (*Geranium robertianum* subsp. *maritimum*), the closely related *G. purpureum*, wood vetch (*Vicia sylvatica*) and blackthorn may be important species here, together with a range of heathland and maritime lichens and mosses. Bracken sometimes invades and becomes dominant, and eventually even heather and bell heather (*Erica cinerea*) may become established. More often, if there is little or no grazing, a scrub with blackthorn, species of bramble, elder, hawthorn and gorse (*Ulex europaeus*) develops as on the dunes. Further succession is unusual, but in southern England it is thought that this scrub could give way to holly (*Ilex aquifolium*) woodland as it does at Dungeness.

II
Sea-cliffs and cliff-tops

Most of the maritime cliffs of north-west Europe are found on coasts exposed to the Atlantic Ocean, from Brittany northwards. The form of the cliffs depends largely on a combination of the strength of the waves eroding the cliff base and the hardness of the rocks. In general, cliffs composed of soft rocks or located on very exposed coasts erode quickly and so tend to be vertical. Such cliffs, with sheer drops of well over 300m in places, are found around the entire coastline, the chalk cliffs on both sides of the English Channel being probably the best-known examples. Where harder rocks are found, or where the wave attack at the cliff base is weak, the cliffs tend to have a bevelled appearance with a vertical lower part and a steep upper slope leading to the cliff top. Most cliffs are of this type. Vertical cliffs tend to have few plants growing on them, except in crevices or on the few ledges that may be present on the cliff face, but bevelled cliffs usually have an extensive cover of plants on their upper slope. For convenience, the term 'cliff' will be used here to cover cliff faces above the intertidal algal vegetation, cliff slopes and cliff tops as far back as maritime vegetation extends.

The most important influence on the vegetation of sea cliffs is the amount of salt-spray deposited on the plants. This can be considerable, equivalent to spreading a layer of salt about 7mm thick in a single year. Maritime species are restricted in their distribution to the coastal fringe. They do not, as might be expected, need salt in order to grow; as with salt-marsh plants, most in fact grow best in ordinary garden soil. However, while most inland plants are intolerant of high salt levels and are often killed by salt-spray, maritime plants grow in these conditions with little loss of vigour. Of course, the tolerance of species, both maritime and inland, to salt does vary. Some common inland species, such as red fescue (*Festuca rubra*) are very tolerant and are unexpectedly common on roadsides where large quantities of de-icing salt

Where ledges on sea-cliffs are manured by seabird droppings, the plants usually grow more luxuriantly. Below the herring gull nest are the yellow flowers of a *Brassica* species, and the white flowers of sea campion (*Silene vulgaris* subsp. *maritima*) together with non-flowering plants of rock samphire (*Crithmum maritimum*), sea beet (*Beta vulgaris* subsp. *maritima*), thrift (*Armeria maritima*) and plantains (*Plantago* species).

are used in winter. Some strictly maritime species, such as the squill, *Scilla verna*, are intolerant of the highest salinities found on cliffs. There is therefore a graded response of species to salt deposition and the plants are arranged in zones depending on distance from the sea—although the zones may be modified by local topographic features. In general, therefore, the headlands that jut out into the Atlantic Ocean and so have the highest salt deposition are those that have the greatest variety of maritime plants.

Cliff crevices

The most salt-tolerant plants are found lowest down on the sea cliffs. They are rooted in crevices between the lichen-covered rocks and form a very distinct zone. The species growing there differ markedly from south to north, reflecting a general division of cliff vegetation into that of southern cliffs (France, England, Wales and southern Ireland) and northern cliffs (Scotland, northern Ireland, the Faeroes, Iceland and Norway). In the south, this zone is characterized by a number of plants most commonly found in the Mediterranean area. Particularly characteristic is rock samphire *(Crithmum maritimum)*, whose grey-green leaves can be found sprouting from the narrowest of crevices. It is a perennial producing fresh flowering stems each year from a rootstock wedged deep in the crevice. Almost always present with rock samphire are the sea-spurrey *Spergularia rupicola*, a fleshy-leaved, pink-flowered, straggly plant, thrift *(Armeria maritima)* and red fescue. These last two are found almost everywhere on sea cliffs but other plants growing with rock samphire vary with the location and geology of the cliffs. Sea aster *(Aster tripolium)* and common scurvy-grass *(Cochlearia officinalis)* are most common on the westernmost cliffs of our region, particularly those of western Ireland. On cliffs that are rich in calcium, usually those of chalk or limestone, the rock samphire is joined by golden samphire *(Inula crithmoides)*, the sea-lavender *Limonium binervosum*, and the grasses *Desmazeria marina* and *Parapholis incurva*.

In the north, rock samphire is replaced by lovage *(Ligusticum scoticum)*. Again, red fescue and thrift are usually present and so, frequently, is roseroot *(Rhodiola rosea)*. One of the characteristic features of these cooler northern cliffs is that mountain plants such as roseroot or alpine mouse-ear *(Cerastium alpinum)* occur at sea level. Associated with both rock samphire and lovage, but usually in deeper crevices under overhanging rocks, is sea spleenwort *(Asplenium marinum)*.

Climate appears to be the reason for the limited distribution of southern cliff species. Sea spleenwort leaves are killed by even very short exposures to temperatures of no lower than —1°C, and many other species cannot survive

winter in the open only a couple of kilometres inland from where they normally grow. Temperatures on the cliffs exposed to the Atlantic rarely or never reach freezing point because the warm waters of the Gulf Stream keep the air just above the sea two or three degrees warmer than it is a mere 500m inland. Lovage is much more tolerant of low temperatures and may be unable to grow further south because the cliffs are too dry.

Not all cliffs, however, have an initial zone of rock-samphire or lovage. On the chalk cliffs on both sides of the English Channel, particularly in the Pas de Calais, this zone has wild cabbage *(Brassica oleracea)*, thought to be the ancestor of the garden vegetable. It is usually found growing with wild carrot *(Daucus carota* subsp. *gummifer)*, scentless mayweed *(Matricaria maritima)*, red fescue and cock's-foot *(Dactylis glomerata)*. A perennial, it forms massive cabbages covered with yellow flowers in the early summer. The other plants form a layer beneath the cabbages. Various plants more usually found on sand-dunes or shingle beaches, such as sea-kale *(Crambe maritima)* and yellow horned-poppy *(Glaucium flavum)*, also occur very occasionally in this zone.

Rock samphire (*Crithmum maritimum*) grows in crevices low on the cliffs. The small flowers are later replaced by corky fruits which can float in sea water for considerable periods of time without any effect on germination. Flowering period: June-August.

The sea aster (*Aster tripolium*) has two forms. The commoner has both lilac ray and yellow disc florets but there is a rarer one with only yellow disc florets. Sea asters are usually found on salt marshes but may grow on sea cliffs in the far west of the region. Flowering period: July-October.

Left: Wild cabbage (*Brassica oleracea*) grows on the edge of calcareous cliffs on either side of the English Channel. Cultivated varieties of cabbage, cauliflower, sprouts and broccoli are probably all derived from this plant. Flowering period: May-August.

On northern cliffs, many mountain plants are found at low altitudes. Here roseroot (*Rhodiola rosea*) is growing in a luxuriant turf of red fescue (*Festuca rubra*) mixed with thrift (*Armeria maritima*). Flowering period: May-August.

The spring squill (*Scilla verna*) is a plant of grassy sea cliffs on the Atlantic coasts of the region, though not western Ireland. Where it is found, it is usually abundant, studding the vegetation with its blue flowers. Flowering period: April–May.

Cliff grasslands

Inland of or above the cliff crevice communities lies a zone of maritime grassland. This develops where soil accumulates first in isolated pockets among the rocks and then as a broad belt. The grassland is almost always dominated by red fescue, particularly towards the seaward edge. Where there is no grazing and the soil is not too thin and dry, the fescue grows as a deep luxuriant turf, in fact it forms a mattress made up of a dense layer of intertwined rhizomes and stems topped by long slender leaves. The fescue is so dense that relatively few other species can be found. Thrift is almost always present and there may be individual plants of common bird's-foot-trefoil (*Lotus corniculatus*), sea campion (*Silene vulgaris* subsp. *maritima*), sea plantain (*Plantago maritima*) and common scurvy-grass. Some of the crevice plants can also be found along the seaward edges. One interesting plant to be found in this fescue turf is wild asparagus (*Asparagus officinalis* subsp. *prostratus*), which is similar to cultivated asparagus except that it grows horizontally within the top layers of the fescue. Its red berries are particularly conspicuous in the autumn.

The fescue mattress is not as common as it might be and is often restricted to inaccessible ledges. This is because it is very sensitive to grazing and many cliffs, particularly in the north, are grazed by sheep and cattle. Where grazing occurs, the turf, although still dominated by red fescue, only grows 1–2 cm high and contains many more species. Thrift is abundant, as are the buck's-horn plantain (*Plantago coronopus*), sea plantain and, farther inland, ribwort plantain (*P. lanceolata*). Other characteristic species of this short turf of fescue and plantains are common bird's-foot-trefoil, white clover (*Trifolium repens*), sea carrot and sea campion. These may be joined by the squill, *Scilla verna*, whose blue flowers stud the grassland in May; the white clover *Trifolium occidentale*, which is common where it occurs but is only found in Cornwall and Brittany; *Primula scotica*, whose bright purple flowers enliven the green on the north coast of Scotland; and occasional hummocks of moss campion (*Silene acaulis*) from there northwards. There are vast areas of this grassland and entire cliff tops can shine with light reflected from the shiny leaves of sea plantain. Where there is extreme exposure to salt-spray coupled with very poor drainage, the turf gains plants characteristic of salt marshes such as sea-milkwort (*Glaux maritima*), the rush *Juncus gerardi* and sea arrowgrass (*Triglochin maritima*). It then resembles a piece of upper salt marsh even though it may be up to 100 m above the sea. Since such a community is found in waterlogged conditions and cliffs are generally dry and well drained, it is dependent on the higher rainfall that occurs in the north of

Left: Scentless mayweed (*Matricaria maritima*) is a common cliff plant particularly where there is nutrient enrichment. Here it grows with a more unusual cliff plant, chives (*Allium schoenoprasum*). Flowering period: June-August.

Below: Buck's-horn plantain (*Plantago coronopus*), which usually grows on sea cliffs, sand dunes and other dry, sandy or gravelly places near the sea, is easily distinguished from other plantains by the narrow lobes on its hairy leaves. Flowering period: May-July.

The coastal race of the wild carrot (*Daucus carota* subsp. *gummifer*) is particularly common in grasslands on the southern cliffs. It is shorter and sturdier than the inland race and has a convex flowering head as opposed to a flat or concave one. Flowering period: June-August.

the British Isles, the Faeroes, Iceland and Norway.

Farther inland, more and more typically inland plants are found while the number of maritime species diminishes. The grasses Yorkshire fog (*Holcus lanatus*), common bent (*Agrostis capillaris*) amd sweet vernal-grass (*Anthoxanthum odoratum*) become more important, particularly in the north. In France and southern England, where the cliffs are relatively dry and warm, red fescue and thrift are accompanied by cock's-foot, sea carrot and common bird's-foot-trefoil together with plants of drier, often calcareous, grasslands such as common restharrow (*Ononis repens*), greater knapweed (*Centaurea scabiosa*), burnct-saxifrage (*Pimpinella saxifraga*), salad burnet (*Sanguisorba minor*) and Nottingham catchfly (*Silene nutans*). The maritime Portland spurge (*Euphorbia portlandica*) is often abundant.

In shady cliff gullies, usually north-facing, where a deep rich soil has accumulated, there is often a very characteristic and luxuriant community consisting of primroses (*Primula vulgaris*) and bluebells (*Hyacinthoides non-scripta*) mixed in with thrift, common scurvy-grass and red fescue. The combination of yellow, blue, pink and white in the spring is particularly attractive. Primroses and bluebells are usually thought of as woodland plants, but, in this habitat, there have never been any trees or shrubs as the level of salt deposition is too high. Inland, bluebells and primroses are largely restricted to woodland because they cannot compete in the open with the vigorous inland grasses. These are, however, intolerant of salt and so do not grow on the cliffs. Competition from cliff species is much less and primroses and bluebells are able to grow there happily.

In the north, higher rainfall and lower evaporation lessen the influence of the incoming salt by diluting it. This means that species that are usually found inland on montane cliff ledges may grow on the higher ledges of the sea cliffs. In Norway, Iceland and the Faeroes, ledges containing a mixture of thrift, sea plantain and common scurvy-grass also include such species as roseroot, mountain sorrel *(Oxyria digyna)*, angelica *(Angelica sylvestris* and *A. archangelica)* and common valerian *(Valeriana officinalis)*.

Cliff heath

Maritime grasslands give way to maritime heath except on the most calcareous soils where they merge with inland calcareous grasslands. The first plants of heather *(Calluna vulgaris)* or bell heather *(Erica cinerea)* are found on the leeward side of grass tussocks or rocks, but a bit farther inland a very characteristic open heathland develops. The almost horizontal plants of heather and bell heather are usually accompanied by sheep's-fescue *(Festuca ovina)* and Yorkshire-fog, together with sea plantain, the squill *Scilla verna*, cat's-ear *(Hypochoeris radicata)*, wild thyme *(Thymus praecox)*, common bird's-foot-trefoil and tormentil *(Potentilla erecta)*. The presence of many other plants is determined by such factors as soil type and latitude. For instance, in the north, crowberry *(Empetrum nigrum)*, cross-leaved heath *(Erica tetralix)* and viviparous fescue *(Festuca vivipara)* are common. In the south, the heaths on moist but well-drained and fertile soils are particularly rich in species. Dyer's greenweed *(Genista tinctoria)* and hairy greenweed *(G. pilosa)* are often present together with a large number of herbaceous plants such as ox-eye daisy *(Leucanthemum vulgare)*, betony *(Stachys officinalis)*, saw-wort *(Serratula tinctoria)*, common dog-violet *(Viola riviniana)*, lady's-bedstraw *(Galium verum)*, dropwort *(Filipendula vulgaris)* and burnet rose *(Rosa pimpinellifolia)*. On drier, shallow soils, many of the maritime plants are present, with thrift, buck's-horn plantain and sea campion being particularly conspicuous, as well as plants of the maritime stonecrop *(Sedum)* community. On more acid rocks, particularly in dry conditions, western gorse *(Ulex gallii)* is abundant. This gives a spectacular display in the late summer when the purples of the heathers are combined with the brilliant yellow of the western gorse. This type of heath is found mainly in the south of England and Wales and in Brittany. Another, usually on slightly more exposed land, is

particularly found in Brittany, where the dominant plant is the yellow-flowered prostrate broom *(Cytisus scoparius* subsp. *prostratus)*.

All cliff heaths are notable for dwarf growth with bushes commonly no more than 20cm tall. The bushes are often arranged in waves at right angles to the prevailing wind since wind-borne salt tends to kill the growth on the windward side of the bush so that it grows steadily downwind. The effects of air turbulence created by the bushes encourage the formation of regular lines and other plants grow in the gaps between. Many of the plants of these exposed maritime heaths, such as the prostrate broom, are genetically dwarf, remaining so when cultivated away from the sea. Dwarfing means that there is less of the plant above the general level of the vegetation and therefore less exposed to the full rigours of the salt-laden wind. The dwarfing usually takes one of two forms: either the stem of the plant is very short but still upright, or the plant grows in a prostrate manner with the stems growing horizontally. Many of the herbaceous plants show the first form: for example, ox-eye daisy, betony and saw-wort have normal sized flowers on stems only 2–3cm tall instead of the usual 20–50cm. Prostrate growth is shown by many of the woody plants and can be seen in juniper *(Juniperus communis)*, broom, dyer's greenweed and hairy greenweed. These can form bushes up to 3–4m across, yet

On the very shallow soils around rocks grow stonecrops (*Sedum* species) and other plants that are capable of surviving drought conditions. Here the white English stonecrop, (*S. anglicum*), with its very succulent leaves, is growing amongst lichen-covered rocks. Flowering period: June-September.

Cliff-top heath can be very spectacular, particularly when the purples of heather (*Calluna vulgaris*) and bell-heather (*Erica cinerea*) are mixed with the yellow of western gorse (*Ulex gallii*). Earlier in the year such a heath would have dotted through it the blue flowers of the squill *Scilla verna*. Flowering period: July-September.

Many quite tall plants become short or prostrate on the cliffs. One example is the prostrate race of broom (*Cytisus scoparius* subsp. *maritimus*) which grows with its shoots tightly pressed against the ground. When in flower, the stems are almost hidden by the yellow blooms. Flowering period: May-June.

only grow about 20 cm tall. It has also been shown that plants growing in the maritime heath may be very much more tolerant of saline conditions than individuals of the same species growing inland.

Amongst the areas of heath and grassland on the cliffs are patches of soil, particularly on or around the edges of rocks, that are very shallow and dry. These small areas support a vegetation of short-lived plants, many of which are winter annuals, such as the grasses *Aira praecox*, *Bromus hordeaceus* subsp. *ferronii*, *Desmazeria marina*, *Parapholis incurva* and the mouse-ear *Cerastium diffusum*. Amongst these plants grow the succulent perennials biting stonecrop (*Sedum acre*), on calcareous soils, and English stonecrop (*S. anglicum*), on acid soils; both are very drought resistant. In the north, such communities are rather uncommon since the moister conditions enable the surrounding grassland or heath vegetation to encroach upon the shallow soils, but in the southernmost parts of our area these communities become increasingly rich. Bulbous plants such as the squill *Scilla autumnalis*, the crocus-like *Romulea columnae* and chives (*Allium schoenoprasum*) grow there as well as annuals such as the diminutive grass *Mibora minima*, the scurvy-grass *Cochlearia danica*, the inconspicuous allseed *Polycarpon tetraphyllum*, the dwarf pansy *Viola kitaibelliana* and several clovers (*Trifolium* species).

Growing in open, often very shallow-soiled areas is the winter annual scurvy grass *Cochlearia danica*. It germinates in the winter, flowers in the spring and by July is usually recognizable only as shrivelled remains. Flowering period: January-May.

Cliff scrub

Shrubs are rather unusual on most cliffs because they are too sensitive to salt to be able to colonize the steep slopes and tops. They would normally form a zone inland of the heaths and grasslands, but usually these areas are suitable for cultivation or have been enclosed for pasture. In fact, on most of the deeper, more fertile cliff tops, the field boundaries are in the grassland or heath zones. However, scrub does occur when the soil is too shallow or too poor for agricultural purposes, or on relatively sheltered coasts where it can colonize the steep cliff slopes. In these conditions there may be dense, impenetrable thickets made up of blackthorn (*Prunus spinosa*), privet (*Ligustrum vulgare*) or gorse (*Ulex europaeus*).

Bird-cliff vegetation

The massed nesting or roosting of seabirds, particularly herring gulls and lesser black-backed gulls (*Larus argentatus* and *L. fuscus*), guillemots (*Uria aalge*) and razorbills (*Alca torda*), have a marked and characteristic effect on the cliff vegetation. In England and France, tree mallow (*Lavatera arborea*), sea beet (*Beta vulgaris* subsp. *maritima*), sea campion, scentless mayweed and the orache *Atriplex*

prostrata are particularly characteristic of bird-cliffs. These plants are fairly robust and can withstand the wear and tear of a bird colony. They are also plants that may require high levels of nutrients, obtained here from bird guano. Sea beet and tree mallow are generally biennials, and situations are known where the vegetation is dominated by flowering sea beet with seedling tree mallow in one year, and by flowering tree mallow and seedling sea beet the next. Tree mallow is known to be sensitive to cold, a factor that restricts this vigorous plant to coastal sites.

In the north, the plants of bird-cliffs are those that require or can withstand high nutrient levels, although they are not restricted to maritime habitats. Chief amongst these are

Thrift (*Armeria maritima*) is characteristic of sea cliffs and salt marshes. Here it is growing in shallow dry soil amongst a number of annual grasses, including *Desmazeria marina* and *Bromus hordeaceus* subsp. *ferronii* which set seed and die by early summer. Flowering period: April-September.

The tree-mallow (*Lavatera arborea*) is a particularly robust plant which can grow as tall as 3 metres. The leaves are softly hairy and the large flowers are rose-purple with deep purple veins. The plant is sensitive to cold and this may be one reason why it is restricted to southern coasts.

common chickweed (*Stellaria media*), cow parsley (*Anthriscus sylvestris*), angelica (*Angelica archangelica*) and red campion (*Silene dioica*). Various grasses, particularly red fescue and Yorkshire-fog thrive in these situations.

Sea cliffs probably represent one of the most natural vegetation types that remain in north-west Europe. As in the mountains, human influence is largely confined to the presence of domestic grazing animals. There may be paths, camping and caravan sites, but these occupy relatively little area, particularly as modern man seems very reluctant to walk more than a few hundred metres from his car. Thus the majority of sea cliffs, with the exception of noted beauty spots, are still relatively undisturbed.

12
Industrial and urban wasteland

Most people believe that industrial development is always harmful to wildlife, destroying plant habitats and preventing recolonization. Although this is generally true, botanists are now finding that industry can actually create new habitats, often more interesting and richer in species than those that have been lost. When this happens, it is difficult to condemn industrial development as harmful just because it causes change. Indeed, we should accept that industry can help nature conservation in many ways and we should learn to exploit fully its potential to do so.

Industrial wasteland tends to consist of tips, which are usually dry, or hollows, which are often wet. Examples of industrial habitats are limestone and chalk quarries, clay pits, sand and gravel workings, canals, railway embankments and tips of various kinds of waste. These often provide a habitat for uncommon and unusual plants. It may seem strange, but some man-made sites are actually protected for their natural history interest and conservation value.

Industrial habitats are of value for other reasons too. The unusual plant habitats provided by spoil heaps from metal mines can tell us much about natural colonization, evolution and soil formation. Whereas natural habitats are notoriously difficult to study because of competition between plants, unknown prehistory and complicated animal and plant interactions, man-made habitats are of known age and are usually ecologically simple.

Until about twenty-five years ago, little thought had been given to the reclamation of areas damaged by industry. The restoration of waste heaps and extraction sites was, in effect, left to nature. Our attitude today, however, is completely different. The planned reclamation of industrial wasteland is recognized to be of great importance, especially in Germany and Britain where dereliction has been particularly extensive and unsightly. Steps are now being taken to clear the backlog of affected sites and prevent further damage. New grassland

Waste-tips can provide surprising habitats for plants normally found elsewhere. Here the horsetail *Equisetum palustre,* usually found in marshes and damp grassland, is growing up the spoil tip of an old lead mine.

and woodland habitats are being created for productive agriculture, public open spaces, forestry and amenity woodlands.

It is important to distinguish between plant communities planted by man, as part of reclamation, and those which have developed naturally. Because of their much greater botanical interest, most of this chapter is concerned with naturally developed sites.

Metal-contaminated habitats

Scientists have long been intrigued by the open but colourful vegetation of metal-contaminated sites. Most of the early studies were carried out in Belgium, Germany, the Netherlands and France where plant communities on mine spoils and smelter wastes were found to consist of a few similar species whatever metal was involved. This association of plants is quite unlike any found in natural habitats. One of its most characteristic species is the calamine pansy *Viola calaminaria*. This pansy, which is very closely related to the common wild pansy *(V. tricolor)* is restricted to soils containing calamine (zinc carbonate).

Commonly growing with calamine pansy are alpine penny-cress *(Thlaspi alpestre)*, spring sandwort *(Minuartia verna)*, bladder and sea campions *(Silene vulgaris* and subsp. *maritima)* and sheep's-fescue *(Festuca ovina)*. This plant association is of special interest for several reasons. The most significant feature is that the mine-waste soils contain toxic concentrations of metals, usually zinc, lead or copper, which prevent other species from colonizing. The mine-waste plants survive because they are resistant to metallic poisoning. However, when plants of the mine-waste species are collected from natural (non-metalliferous) soils and transplanted into metalliferous soils, virtually all die, indicating that metal tolerance is not a normal characteristic even in these species but appears as a result of selection. Only a few species have evolved such resistant races and this is the reason why the floras of metalliferous habitats are so restricted.

Another remarkable feature of these plants is that they can accumulate very large amounts of metals in their shoots and leaves without sustaining damage. The metals are taken up through the roots and concentrations in the leaves sometimes exceed those in the soils around them. Zinc concentrations in excess of the normal figure of 0.01 per cent have been found in most of the plants mentioned above and up to 0.8 per cent has been recorded in alpine penny-cress.

Other metal-resistant herbs include ribwort plantain *(Plantago lanceolata)*, thrift or sea pink *(Armeria maritima)*, fairy flax *(Linum catharticum)*, harebell *(Campanula rotundifolia)*, dandelion *(Taraxacum officinale)*, coltsfoot

Some plants have evolved a remarkable resistance to toxicity caused by ores discarded during mining. Here the spring sandwort *(Minuartia verna)* is growing on ground so contaminated by lead and zinc that almost no other plants can survive. Flowering period: May-September.

Right: Often a single species may completely dominate a habitat. Here the common poppy *(Papaver rhoeas)* covers waste-tips from iron-ore mining. Flowering period: June-August.

Orchids can be surprisingly common on waste sites. Here the dark red helleborine *(Epipactis atrorubens)* is growing on iron-ore powder: its normal habitat is limestone rocks and screes. Flowering period: June-July.

Coltsfoot (*Tussilago farfara*) is a very common colonist of a variety of waste habitats. It is fairly metal-tolerant, and especially characteristic of heavy, often waterlogged and compacted soils and clays. The plant flowers before its leaves have appeared. Flowering period: March-April.

(*Tussilago farfara*), monkey flower (*Mimulus guttatus*) and common sorrel *(Rumex acetosa)*. Grasses with similar tolerant races are the common, creeping and brown bents *(Agrostis capillaris, A. stolonifera* and *A. canina)*, sheep's-fescue, red fescue (*Festuca rubra*), Yorkshire-fog *(Holcus lanatus)* and sweet vernal-grass (*Anthoxanthum odoratum*).

It has been proved that tolerance is specific to certain metals. For example, grasses growing on zinc-mine spoil are tolerant of zinc but not necessarily of copper. However, they are often also tolerant of lead because zinc-mine wastes commonly contain toxic amounts of lead.

The soils of metalliferous tips are extremely infertile, being very low in the important plant nutrients nitrogen and phosphorus and having little or no humus or organic matter. As well as possessing metal tolerance, mine-spoil plants are tolerant of low phosphorus. They also tend to grow more slowly, to be smaller than non-tolerant plants and to be more resistant to exposure and drought. All these characteristics are inherited independently of metal tolerance but are very necessary for fitting the plants to their harsh habitats.

Not all metal-mine wastes are toxic to plants because rock surrounding the metalliferous veins, low grade ores and unmineralized vein materials are often tipped on the surface. In Britain several species which are quite uncommon both locally and regionally occur on such tips, particularly on calcareous wastes but occasionally on acidic ones. Examples

Left: Not all waste material is toxic. That of chalk and limestone quarries often differs little from their surrounding soils and is rapidly colonized, sometimes by rather unusual plants such as the white mullein (*Verbascum lychnitis*). This plant can have either white or yellow flowers. Flowering period: July-August.

Right: The devil's-bit scabious *(Succisa pratensis)* is distinguished from other species of scabious in the region by having a four-lobed corolla and undivided, hairy leaves. It is usually found in moist, often acid places in grasslands, heaths and woods, as well as in fens, though it can occur on industrial wastes. Flowering period: June-October.

are the orchids—dark-red helleborine *(Epipactis atrorubens)*, common helleborine *(E. helleborine)*, narrow-lipped helleborine *(E. leptochila)*, green-flowered helleborine *(E. phyllanthes)* and frog orchid *(Coeloglossum viride)*; grass-of-Parnassus *(Parnassia palustris)*, maiden pink *(Dianthus deltoides)* and forked spleenwort *(Asplenium septentrionale)*.

Lime waste habitats

Wastes from chemical industries can be even more extreme than metal-mine spoils yet certain types have formed some of the most interesting of all known industrial habitats. Lime wastes from alkali works favour the growth of many unusual and uncommon plants including wild orchids, providing an unexpected refuge.

Some knowledge of industrial archaeology is necessary to understand the origin of some of these habitats. Until the beginning of this century, washing soda (sodium carbonate) for the chemical industry was manufactured from sodium sulphate, coal and limestone by the Leblanc process. Used throughout Europe, this process caused severe air pollution as well as producing unsightly and intensely alkaline wastes. At first, the wastes were far too alkaline to support any form of plant life but gradually, under the influence of rainfall and carbon dioxide in the atmosphere, the free lime (calcium

hydroxide) disappeared from the surface. This left behind a very limy material which favoured the growth of calcicole plants.

After about 1919, the Leblanc process was replaced by the Solvay or Ammonia Soda process which produces sodium carbonate from salt, ammonia and limestone. This again generates vast quantities of lime waste which have formed more recent lime-rich industrial habitats.

Lime wastes are rich in species because they have the right combination of high lime content and low fertility. Low nitrogen and phosphorus restrict the growth of grasses and clovers which would otherwise suppress the more interesting and uncommon plants. The vegetation is, therefore, always

Left: Lime-wastes are usually colonized by plants characteristic of the most calcareous grasslands, though these may not necessarily be calcicoles. Such a plant is the common centaury (*Centaurium erythraea*). Flowering period: June-October.

Below: Slag from steel works resembles in many ways a coarse limestone, so it is not surprising that it supports plants that grow equally well on limestone quarry waste. These include the biennial carline thistle (*Carlina vulgaris*). Flowering period: July-September.

very open or sparse, allowing slow-growing plants, such as orchids, to colonize and form large populations.

Species characteristic of lime-waste vegetation include certain common grasses such as sheep's-fescue, red fescue, cocks-foot (*Dactylis glomerata*) and creeping bent, which can tolerate alkaline soils. Various calcicole plants such as fairy flax are very common indeed and the following colourful herbs are typical colonizers of the sites: common knapweed (*Centaurea nigra*), coltsfoot, wild angelica (*Angelica sylvestris*), common centaury (*Centaurium erythraea*), blue fleabane (*Erigeron acer*), blue-eyed grass (*Sisyrinchium bermudiana*), mouse-ear hawkweed (*Hieracium pilosella*), common hawkweed (*H. vulgatum*), eyebright (*Euphrasia nemorosa*) and devil's-bit scabious (*Succisa pratensis*). Shrubs include hawthorn (*Crataegus monogyna*), goat willow (*Salix caprea*), creeping willow (*S. repens*), grey willow (*S. cinerea*) and silver birch (*Betula pendula*).

Orchids are often a spectacular feature of such sites. Marsh orchids (*Dactylorhiza incarnata*, *D. majalis* subsp. *praetermissa* and subsp. *purpurella*) are characteristic of most of the habitats but several others occur, including common spotted-orchid (*Dactylorhiza fuchsii*), fragrant orchid (*Gymnadenia conopsea*), early-purple orchid (*Orchis mascula*), marsh helleborine (*Epipactis palustris*) and

pyramidal orchid (*Anacamptis pyramidalis*). The marsh and fragrant orchids are often present in immense colonies of up to 20,000 flowering plants, 100 to the square metre.

Some of the Leblanc waste sites contain patches of markedly different vegetation consisting of species found on very acidic soils. Here there are very few species, typically only wavy hair-grass (*Deschampsia flexuosa*), mat-grass (*Nardus stricta*), common bent and sheep's sorrel (*Rumex acetosella*). The change from a species-rich, lime-waste flora to the acid-loving flora is generally abrupt, and is caused by thin layers of acidic boiler ash overlying the lime waste.

Lime wastes are often discarded from other types of industrial operation but usually on a much smaller scale. Tips of lime-kiln waste, limestone tailings and rubble, calcareous sands and limestone ballast often support similar communities of calcicole plants. Quite extensive, and providing very similar habitats, are tips of blast-furnace slag and the floors of old limestone and chalk quarries. Blast-furnace slag (the waste from the smelting of iron ore with limestone to produce pig iron) weathers to form a very coarse, rocky material closely resembling natural limestone. This slag supports many of the characteristic calcicole plants of the lime-waste tips, notably fairy flax, blue fleabane, common centaury and carline thistle (*Carlina vulgaris*). These often grow in limestone and chalk quarries which

Orchids can colonize waste tips with remarkable speed. Here wet ash from a power station has been invaded by marsh orchids (*Dactylorhiza* species and hybrids) as well as willow (*Salix*) scrub. Flowering period: May-July.

likewise provide habitats for several uncommon orchids such as the bee orchid (*Ophrys apifera*), fly orchid (*O. insectifera*), man orchid (*Aceras anthropophorum*), musk orchid (*Herminium monorchis*) and dark-red helleborine (*Epipactis atrorubens*).

In time, these lime wastes are invaded by hawthorns and willows which may form dense scrub. The increasing shade and improved soil fertility caused by leaf fall and humus enrichment gradually eliminate many of the interesting pioneer plants. The same thing happens when the indigenous grasses are stimulated with artificial fertilizers and flourish at the expense of other species. To retain the pioneer plants it may even be necessary to expose areas of unweathered waste so that natural colonization can begin afresh.

Power station ash habitats

The waste from power stations which burn pulverized coal is known as pulverized fuel ash and often contains high concentrations of borate and soluble salts which are toxic to plant life. Sometimes, however, the ash is quite innocuous and may have an appreciable lime content as, for example, at the lignite-burning power stations in Germany.

One ash site in north-west England has developed a remarkable orchid-rich flora within a period of fifteen years, underlining the speed at which nature can exploit a habitat. There are dense populations of several orchids, particularly marsh orchids, common spotted-orchid and marsh helleborine, as well as centaury and gipsywort (*Lycopus europaeus*). These grow in the more open clearings between patches of willow scrub.

Apart from the orchids, however, the flora differs from that of lime-waste tips because of the considerably lower lime content of the ash. The fine-leaved red and sheep's-fescues are not in evidence and the characteristic calcicole plants such as fairy flax, blue fleabane and carline thistle are also absent. Clovers (*Trifolium* species) are locally frequent and the vegetation is denser. Willow scrub develops rapidly and indicates that the orchid-rich communities may ultimately be overwhelmed and may disappear.

Because of their plumed, wind-blown fruits, thistles are able to colonize rapidly many waste and disturbed sites. The spear thistle *(Cirsium vulgare)* (left) is a biennial, forming a spiny basal rosette of leaves in its first year and then flowering and fruiting in the second year. The smaller-flowered creeping thistle *(Cirsium arvense)* is a perennial which often forms dense patches. Flowering period: July-October.

Many urban waste sites have no particular deficiencies or toxicities and so can be colonized by any plants capable of reaching them (above left). Plants with light, wind-blown seeds have an obvious advantage and rosebay willowherb *(Epilobium angustifolium)* (above) is often a successful invader. Flowering period: July-September.

Saline habitats

Inland salt marshes are very rare throughout north-west Europe. They were originally caused by natural brine springs, many of which have been destroyed. However, the salt industry has created new salt marshes in two ways. The first is the consequence of brine spillage near the works or from pipelines some distance away. The second is the result of subsidence caused by the underground pumping of brine; this has caused the local development of quite large brine pools and salt marshes.

Because inland salt marshes are isolated from the coastal sites, it is difficult for the seed of salt-tolerant species (halophytes) to reach the industrial sites and only a few of the rich variety of salt-marsh plants occur there. The most widespread and abundant plants include a species of orache *(Atriplex prostrata)*, the salt marsh-grass *Puccinellia distans*, a sea-spurrey *Spergularia marina*, sea-aster *(Aster tripolium)* sea arrowgrass *(Triglochin maritima)*, the sedge-like *Scirpus maritimus* and, in mainland Europe but not in Britain, glasswort *(Salicornia* species).

Acidic habitats: colliery spoil

The industrial habitats considered so far provide considerable opportunities for wildlife colonization. In contrast, acidic wastes are colonized, if at all, by very few species. Perhaps the best example is colliery spoil which is often intensely acidic due to the oxidation of iron pyrites. This releases dilute sulphuric acid into the soil over a very long period, sometimes preventing colonization for over a hundred years.

One of the most acid-tolerant grasses found throughout Europe is wavy hair-grass and this is often the sole colonizer of the more acidic spoil tips, forming a complete cover except where the acidity is too intense. If acidity is less extreme, it is joined by several other grasses including the acid-tolerant mat-grass, common bent, Yorkshire-fog and creeping soft-grass *(Holcus mollis)*. Less tolerant grasses which may occur locally are red fescue, sheep's-fescue and the reed-like grass *Calamagrostis epigejos*.

Of the herbs, sheep's sorrel is probably the most acid-tolerant. Less tolerant but often abundant are rosebay willowherb *(Epilobium angustifolium)*, various hawkweeds *(Hieracium* species), creeping thistle *(Cirsium arvense)* and coltsfoot. The evening-primrose *Oenothera biennis* is common in mainland Europe.

Only a few trees and shrubs are sufficiently tolerant of high acidity to be able to invade these sites. Willows, whose airborne seeds give them ready access to sites, are prevalent on many types of wasteland. Silver birch *(Betula pendula)*, sessile oak *(Quercus petraea)* and aspen *(Populus tremula)* may also grow and acacia *(Robinia pseudacacia)* is a feature of European mainland sites. Bramble *(Rubus fruticosus)* often occurs on open ground and under trees.

Given time, these acidic sites develop into either acid heathland or birch-oak woodland. Although poor in species, such habitats may be worthy of conservation, particularly if there are no similar natural habitats nearby.

Urban habitats

Many urban habitats, such as municipal refuse tips, demolition sites and disused railway sidings, are neither toxic nor particularly infertile. Consequently, they are soon invaded by a wide range of weeds, including herbs and grasses. The former usually predominate and tend to be species which have effective seed dispersal and rapid vegetative spread. Rosebay willowherb and thistles *(Cirsium arvense, C. vulgare)* are good examples. It is not surprising, therefore, that many are common garden weeds such as ragwort *(Senecio jacobaea)*, Oxford ragwort *(S. squalidus)*, groundsel *(S. vulgaris)*, coltsfoot, mugwort *(Artemisia vulgaris)*, sow-thistles *(Sonchus* species), dandelion *(Taraxacum* species), annual meadow-grass *(Poa annua)* and field horsetail *(Equisetum arvense)*.

Reclamation

Substantial efforts have been made to establish useful vegetation on industrial wasteland, particularly on colliery spoil. Notable reclamation work has been done in parts of the Rhineland, Ruhr Basin, Westphalia and Cologne lignite districts. Lignite spoils in Denmark have been planted with trees and shrubs, 460 species having been tested in an arboretum which covers 20 hectares of the largest Danish strip-mined lignite field. In Britain, large-scale reclamation work now covers all the main coalfields.

There are two main approaches to reclamation. One involves selecting tolerant trees, shrubs and herbs which are planted directly into the wasteland soils, sometimes with fertilizers and lime. The other entails reshaping the landscape

The evening primrose *Oenothera biennis* was introduced into Europe from north America, and has become naturalized, especially on dunes. It is able to tolerate acidic conditions and it has become a common plant on colliery spoil tips. Its flowers open in the evening and are visited by moths. Flowering period: June-September.

Above: Like some other wasteland plants, Oxford ragwort (*Senecio squalidus*) is an introduced species that has spread rapidly in urban areas. Flowering period: May-December.

Below: Sow thistles (*Sonchus arvensis*) grow in various grassland habitats but have also successfully colonized open urban sites. Flowering period: July-October.

The North American lupin *Lupinus arboreus* grows well on industrial waste covered by a layer of infertile subsoil. Because of its ability to fix atmospheric nitrogen and so improve soil fertility, the plant is often used to reclaim colliery spoil tips in Germany. Flowering period: June-September.

with heavy machinery. This is followed by soil treatment with lime, fertilizer, manure and other materials.

The first method has been used extensively, particularly in earlier reclamation work for tree-planting. The most suitable trees and shrubs are those which are tolerant of acidity, low fertility and waterlogging or drought. Some of the most successful have already been mentioned. Others include the alders *(Alnus glutinosa, A. incana)*, Scots pine *(Pinus sylvestris)* and the North American lupin *Lupinus arboreus*. The alders, acacia and lupins are important as they add nitrogen to the soil by means of nitrogen-fixing bacteria in their root nodules. Once woodland is established, a wider range of species can be introduced because of the shelter provided and the improvement in soil fertility.

The second method, that of reshaping the wasteland, enables new features and habitats to be created. It is vitally important to smooth the contours of tips so that cultivation machinery can prepare the surface and spread lime and fertilizers. Reclamation of acidic colliery spoil, for example, involves extremely heavy liming of up to 200 tonnes per hectare, ripping or deep ploughing to incorporate the lime and relieve compaction, rotavation or harrowing to create a workable soil, the addition of fertilizers, especially nitrogen and phosphorus, and the seeding of pioneer species, including clovers to improve the nitrogen content.

Because acidity is often extreme, liming tends to be the most expensive part of the cultivation treatment. In Germany, the ash from lignite-burning power stations has a very high lime content and has been employed as a more effective and less costly neutralizing agent.

In this chapter it has been possible to describe only a few of the more extreme and interesting types of industrial habitat. However, there is an enormous range of such habitats and immense scope both for further natural colonization and for reclamation. There seems a very good case for letting some sites revert to nature, but where conditions are very unfavourable and unsightly, deliberate reclamation is essential if the landscape is to be made attractive and useful.

13
Threats and conservation

Until the Neolithic period, about 5000 years ago, changes in plant communities were mostly gradual, the result of climatic changes and natural plant succession, such as the progressive colonization of open water. A recurrent theme in many of the preceding chapters has been the profound effect of man on his environment. Since Neolithic times, he has influenced it at an ever increasing rate with the result that over much of north-west Europe most of the habitats are to a greater or lesser extent artificial. Threats to the existing natural and semi-natural vegetation are not just the obvious ones such as industry and building, but can result also from the application of modern methods of farming and forestry, or even from apparently beneficial schemes such as drainage and flood prevention. To counter these threats, conservation is concerned with preserving the best possible examples of such natural and semi-natural vegetation as still exist, and with attempts to ensure that modern developments have the minimal impact on the natural scene.

Agriculture

Much of the lowland countryside in north-west Europe has long been dominated by farming. Until recently the tranquil scene of meadows, hedgerows and copses was an inspiration for poets and writers and its wildlife was studied and enjoyed by generations of naturalists. Even now there are many who not only regard the agricultural scene as an improvement on nature but believe that farming has not had, and indeed cannot have, a harmful effect on wildlife. Unfortunately much has changed in agricultural practice in the last half century. Like all industries, farming has had to become ever more competitive and efficient. Increased efficiency demands that a larger area of land be farmed and that output from existing land be improved; furthermore, the techniques which are available to today's farmer are infinitely more dangerous to wildlife than traditional farming practices.

Primroses *(Primula vulgaris)* are threatened in two ways. Agricultural improvements and woodland clearance are removing the habitat and 'flower-lovers' are digging the plants up to transfer to their gardens. Flowering period: January-May.

In the past deforestation has been the most dramatic result of the demand for agricultural land. Much of the natural deciduous forest cover of north-west Europe has disappeared and been replaced by arable fields and grasslands in the lowlands and by sheep-grazed moorlands in the uplands. This destruction is still continuing. Deciduous woods and copses are rarely considered to be economically viable and they are one by one disappearing. In Britain and western France, where hedgerows are a traditional form of field boundary, these too are vanishing, particularly in the most intensively farmed lowland areas where efficiency demands ever larger fields. In one area of eastern England the length of hedgerows is less than a quarter of what it was at the end of the second world war. Yet the importance to wildlife of lowland hedgerows is considerable. In areas where woodlands have all but disappeared, they represent the only available habitat for woodland plants and animals.

Herbicides have been used with such effect that on the more efficient farms it is now rare to find a field with a rich weed flora. A particularly disturbing aspect of herbicide use is the way in which, through carelessness, the spray is allowed to drift onto the surrounding hedgerows and other marginal vegetation and so impoverish their flora. A similar alarming development in the British Isles is experimental aerial spraying of bracken-infested uplands, using a herbicide which is by no means specific to bracken. Because of these changes, some of the most intensively farmed lowland arable areas of western Europe have lost almost all their wild plants and their associated animals, except in a few isolated nature reserves and along roadside verges.

Perhaps the most important threat at the present time, however, is the drainage and destruction of wetlands, particularly inland mires and coastal marshes. The continued drainage of mires and poor quality land has assumed very serious proportions. In an attempt to minimize flooding and improve drainage, rivers are straightened and deepened, the river bed is dredged and the mud deposited on the vegetation along its banks; riverside trees and shrubs are removed. Apart from the direct effects on the rivers themselves, these and other associated drainage works have tended to lower the water table of low-lying areas so that even wetland reserves may be threatened and may require artificial pumping to restore the water table. Shrinkage and oxidation of the peat may also be a problem in these areas, posing a continuing threat to the remaining wetlands.

A recent threat to aquatic vegetation is the alarming practice of applying herbicides to control both the emergent and submerged plant life but there are other, less direct dangers. Increased crop yields require the extensive and intensive use of fertilizers and herbicides. Considerable quantities of these fertilizers are washed by rain into natural

If high levels of fertilizer are used over long periods, dandelions may become the dominant species in hay meadows (right) as other flowers are eliminated. The dandelion's plumed fruits (above) result in efficient distribution so that they can rapidly colonize any bare, reasonably fertile soils. Flowering period: March-October.

waters and this, together with enrichment from sewage effluents, alters their flora. The algae in the waters multiply greatly to form a dense layer at the water surface, reducing the light that reaches the submerged plants, which consequently die. The death and decay of the increased numbers of algae reduces the oxygen content of the water until hardly anything can survive. A classic example of this is the virtual sterilization of the botanically famous Broadland area of East Anglia.

Coastal reclamation may have very serious consequences for bird life as estuarine salt marshes are vital for migrating wildfowl and waders. These birds require a chain of such sites and the reclamation of only a few may seriously jeopardize the successful migration and the survival of certain species.

The combined effect of fertilizers and herbicides is to promote uniformity. Traditionally managed semi-natural grasslands, fertilized only by animal droppings, have a rich herb flora. The effect of the high levels of artificial fertilizers generally used now is to favour the more productive agriculturally important grasses, at the expense of the slower-growing grasses and herbaceous plants. Eventually even the grasses may be eliminated to give a sward of dandelions (*Taraxacum* species) and broad-leaved dock (*Rumex obtusifolius*).

A similar effect is achieved by ploughing up old species-rich pasture, sometimes after killing the existing plants with a general herbicide, and reseeding with a mixture of selected grass strains.

Right: The common poppy (*Papaver rhoeas*) is a weed of arable fields and waste places, commonest in the south of our region, but becoming progressively rare towards the north. It can easily be distinguished from other red poppies by its hairless round capsule. Flowering period: June-August.

Left: Drainage of lowland mires to increase agricultural land has a dramatic effect on wetland species. The clubmoss *Lycopodium inundatum* is becoming increasingly scarce in the region.

The improved productivity of grazing land allows more animals to be kept, but increasing the stocking rates without improving the grazing often greatly impoverishes the grassland and eventually diminishes the value of the land to the farmer as well. As mentioned in Chapter 4, overgrazing of the upland bent-fescue grasslands usually results in the dominance of the unpalatable mat-grass.

Many of these agricultural practices, for example drainage, ploughing and re-seeding, qualify for grant-aid, either nationally or from a wide variety of funds available for farm improvement schemes and administered by the European Economic Community. Many of these are aimed specifically at farmers of marginal land, where the confrontation between conservationists and farmers attempting to wrest a living from poor quality land is most acute.

Forestry

The major threats from commercial forestry today arise not so much from deforestation as from the management of existing woodlands and the afforestation of treeless habitats.

As explained in Chapter 2, the familiar deciduous woodlands of Europe, with their associated varied ground flora and shrubs, were often artificially created, especially in the British Isles, the products of forestry economics which no longer apply. Deciduous trees take longer to mature than conifers and, despite higher hardwood planting grants, the economic attractions of conifers, with their rapid growth and multiplicity of uses, mean that deciduous woodlands are being increasingly replaced by conifers.

Commercial forestry is really a form of agriculture, concerned with obtaining the maximum yield from a long-lived, even-aged crop. In commercial plantations the land has to be prepared ready for seedling establishment, kept free from weeds (which may be other trees) in the early stages, and managed in a way that will permit access to the large vehicles involved in thinning and harvesting. The young conifers are planted close together and grow up to produce a virtually impenetrable thicket of saplings. These are progressively thinned but, except in deciduous larch plantations, very little light penetrates to the woodland floor which is consequently almost, if not entirely, devoid of vegetation. The plantations are clear-felled in blocks when mature, but this is considerably before the end of their natural life-span, so that in normal conditions no gaps ever form in the canopy from the death and natural collapse of individual trees. Only a few species are therefore able to colonize the woodland floor which is covered by a slowly decaying acidic mat of needles. The acid humus also brings about a progressive deterioration in the nutrient and physical conditions of the soil. Sometimes these plantations of

The corncockle (*Agrostemma githago*) is only known as a cornfield weed, apparently having no natural habitat. Now that seed grain is efficiently cleaned of weed seeds, it is very likely to become extinct unless measures are taken to preserve it. Flowering period: June-August.

Right: The once common cornflower (*Centaurea cyanus*) is becoming very rare and is now only easily found in areas where agriculture is still relatively backward. Flowering period: June-August.

conifers may be relieved by plantings of beech (*Fagus sylvatica*) and sycamore (*Acer pseudoplatanus*), the only two deciduous trees which are at all widely grown for their timber as well as for their amenity value. In the British Isles sycamore is an alien tree while beech is native only in southern England. If they replace or are planted in deciduous woodland they have an adverse effect on the ground flora because they cast a deep shade, have a vigorous rooting system and produce a deep litter which, in the case of beech, is slow to decay.

Economic pressures mean that in the native coniferous forests of Fennoscandia it is no longer possible to achieve an economic return by the felling of individually selected mature trees. The solution is to clear-fell and replant, with all the damage that these forestry operations necessarily entail. Nevertheless, if the forests are not too intensively managed, most of the dwarf shrub, lichen and moss communities are able to persist; this is in sharp contrast to the intensively managed coniferous plantations farther south which replace deciduous woodlands. As with farming, the use of herbicides is a matter of increasing public concern, particularly the aerial spraying of young plantations to kill the developing broad-leaved herbs and shrubs and undesirable tree seedlings which threaten to stifle the initially slower-growing conifers.

The afforestation of open, tree-less land is very much a

Limestone quarrying can be a particular threat to wild flowers since it is limestone areas that carry the richest vegetation in terms of numbers of species. Modern quarries are very efficient, large scale operations and leave little debris or soil for displaced species to colonize.

feature of forestry in the British Isles. For this to be an economic proposition, the land has to be acquired relatively cheaply and this means that it is usually hill pasture and moorland. Vast areas of the uplands are now covered with coniferous plantations with the almost total loss of the original plant communities. Although these communities are often very widespread and support few plant species, they may be important breeding areas for moorland birds such as the golden plover (*Charadrius apricarius*) and merlin (*Falco columbarius*). The most important botanical sites which are lost are areas of wetland which disappear as adjacent slopes are drained and forested.

The British are very resentful of any intrusion into an open landscape and many amenity organizations have been vociferous in their opposition to afforestation—usually, but not always, with conifers. Yet most of the newly afforested areas were once covered with deciduous trees, in some places into the present century. A further objection to coniferous afforestation is the geometric, unnatural appearance of the plantations. Fortunately public opinion has been effective and, particularly in the more attractive upland areas, the state forestry service, at least, now attempts to soften the outlines by allowing conifers and wild birch to regenerate naturally above the upper limits of the plantations and by retaining any native deciduous trees growing along hillside streams.

Industrialization and pollution

The pace of industrialization and the pursuit of an ever-increasing standard of living has naturally generated a voracious demand for land for houses, new towns, industrial sites and roads. These developments are generally at the expense of farmland and amenity areas around existing towns. One example where urban development is having a serious effect is in southern Finland where the spread of Helsinki and other towns along the south coast has made serious inroads into the fragmentary areas of deciduous woodland which is here at its northern limit.

The increasing standard of living leading to the acquisition of holiday homes has also had a serious impact in some countries, for example Denmark and western France, where some of the best fixed dunes have been destroyed by uncontrolled building.

Of more concern for the botanist are the effects of the so-called extractive industries. Their demands are a barometer of industrial health and one of the few advantages of the present-day industrial recession is that these demands have tended to stabilize or even decline. The main industries concerned are the extraction of sand and gravel, the open-cast mining of iron-ore and coal, and quarrying, especially for chalk and limestone. Until the recent recession, increasing

When lakes are converted to reservoirs, the submerged and marginal vegetation usually disappears as there is no longer a stable water level. The fluctuating level causes a pale, sterile rim around the reservoir, which is very obvious when the water is low.

Right: Water pollution and the clearance by mechanical means and herbicides of the vegetation in and alongside drainage ditches and rivers has resulted in the decline of many aquatic and marsh plants. Here the increasingly rare water violet (*Hottonia palustris*) is growing with the yellow cress (*Rorippa amphibia*) in a nature reserve. Flowering period: May-June.

demands and improved techniques led to old sites being re-opened and new ones developed. Old sites have, over the years, become increasingly important as sanctuaries for wildlife in a lowland agricultural landscape. This is especially true of old limestone and chalk quarries. The new quarries are on a very different scale, both in area and depth. The variety of plant life on chalk and limestone has already been emphasized several times and the demand for these rocks has created serious conservation problems in many areas, with opposition to further quarrying coming both from naturalists and amenity bodies. The need for adequate supplies of limestone and chalk is of course accepted; the issue is how to quantify this need. Unlike most rocks, chalk and limestone are relatively pure chemicals and as such they are used, for example, in cement, glass, iron and steel-making, and as a fertilizer. It is argued that, because of their conservation importance, these rocks should be used almost exclusively for these purposes. Yet 80 per cent of British limestone production is used as aggregate even though other suitable rocks are often available.

Another natural resource in great demand is water. As demand increases, rivers have to be regulated to ensure sufficient supply throughout the year. Reservoirs are built and, whether they are completely new areas of water or formed from existing lakes, land must be flooded. Reservoirs

are often unsatisfactory habitats for aquatic plants, few of which are able to survive prolonged exposure during periods of low water levels. As a result, upland reservoirs, in particular, usually show a conspicuous rim during these periods, colonized only by ephemeral mosses. Conditions around lowland reservoirs may be more suitable and the rim may be covered with plants if the low water level lasts for a considerable period. When further water supplies are required, it is often cheaper to divert water from neighbouring rivers into an existing reservoir than to construct a new one. This has been done on a vast scale in northern Sweden where only a few rivers now remain in a natural, unregulated state. When water is diverted in this way, only a small amount of 'compensation' water is left flowing down the original river. Regulating the flow of a river may have a profound affect on the ecology not only of the river, but also of the surrounding land. The annual fluctuations in water level are reduced, the river level is lower, flooding disappears and the river bed is no longer scoured by winter spates or spring melt-water. The pumping of water from subterranean reservoirs (aquifers) in porous rock could have serious consequences in the future as it results in a general lowering of the water table. It is already known to have caused a number of chalk streams in southern England to run dry.

More extensive and insidious is the threat to aquatic plant and animal life from pollution by industrial and sewage effluent, the run-off of agricultural fertilizers and the effects of herbicides. All these factors have probably contributed to the decline of submerged plants, particularly in the lower reaches of rivers. Two of the species showing marked declines in recent years are frog-bit *(Hydrocharis morsus-ranae)* and water violet *(Hottonia palustris)*. Clearing and deepening ditches mechanically instead of by hand has probably also contributed to their reduction. Even in the English Lake District pollution is almost certainly responsible for the extinction of *Hydrilla verticillata*, a delicate submerged plant which elsewhere in Europe is now known only from a single Irish lake and scattered sites from north-east Germany to Lithuania.

Aerial pollution has, as yet, had a less dramatic impact even though lichens have been disappearing from towns and cities for more than a century. Of increasing concern at the present time are emissions, particularly of sulphur dioxide, from the chimneys of power stations. It is now well established that such emissions from the industrial areas of England and the Ruhr are responsible for acidifying the rain over large parts of Scandinavia with consequent harmful effects on the animal life of lakes. There is at the moment little evidence of an adverse effect on the plant life, either of lakes or on land.

Recreation and tourism

Another pressure on the countryside comes from the dramatic increase in leisure time, leisure facilities and personal mobility, especially since the second world war. This has meant additional tourist facilities, with salt marshes and lake shores converted to marinas and woodland to 'well-screened' caravan sites. Apart from these developments there has been an inevitable increase in the trampling, disturbance and erosion of sensitive sites, such as heathland and, especially, sand-dunes. Here the all-important cover of marram grass may be sufficiently weakened to allow blow-outs to develop. Tourist pressure on dune systems may reach astonishing levels. Rømø is a typical sand-dune island in the north Friesian Islands of Denmark, only 16km by 7km. Every summer its population of 900 is swollen to 100,000 by an invasion of tourists. In these popular islands cars, caravan sites, pony trekking and walking break up the delicate plant cover, the rare plants being especially vulnerable. To make matters worse, on most of these islands the increasing extraction of fresh water from the diminishing store below the dunes is lowering the water table and leading to a drying-out of the dune slacks.

Rivers and lakes may also be affected by boating, a rapidly growing leisure activity. Powered boats pollute the water with their fuel, and, usually illegally, by the discharge of sewage; their wake erodes the banks, especially of rivers, and the propellors tear up the submerged plants. Even moored boats can affect the vegetation by completely shading it out from the whole area over which they are free to move.

Conservation

The threats to natural and semi-natural vegetation described here and in the previous chapters are clearly the result of the economic demands of western civilization from which we all benefit to varying extents in terms of improved food supply, living conditions and health. Conservation of the remaining natural wild areas will therefore at some point affect the rate of economic development. Can we justify such constraints? The exodus from the cities at weekends and holidays clearly indicates that the countryside with its diversity of wildlife satisfies a human need of being part of a larger biological community. A world which contained no plants or animals except those currently used in agriculture would be close indeed to the drabness envisaged by George Orwell in *Nineteen Eighty-four* and some writers have questioned whether the human race could survive such a destruction of the natural system.

There are also other reasons for maintaining the diversity of the natural world; at present we exploit comparatively few species although in the past many more were used. For example a wide variety of plants were formerly employed for medical purposes. Recent studies have shown that many wild species may be valuable, either because they have qualities which can be introduced into those species which we exploit today, or because they have useful products themselves. Our experiences with herbicides and pesticides over the past thirty years have shown us that we are unlikely to completely protect our crops from weeds, diseases and pests purely by chemical means and that checks through natural predators will remain an important means of control. If unchecked, the present trends will lead to a progressive reduction both in species diversity and population numbers. Only the most strenuous efforts will maintain the present position without further deterioration, and an overall advance may never be possible.

One of the few encouraging developments has been the rapid rise in size and influence of the conservation movement. The level of interest in conservation has increased steadily over the last twenty years, partly as a response to the accelerating destruction of natural habitats and partly as a reaction to the general despoilation and pollution of the countryside. It is a movement that governments cannot easily ignore, and most political parties pay lip service at least to the desirability of conservation.

In practice, however, a government has to weigh the cost of conservationists' idealism against practical politics and economics. As a result state support for conservation is all too often limited to relatively uncontentious and inexpensive schemes. The direct influence of governments may be seen in several ways.

Firstly there is the direct support of a national conservation body, its effectiveness and range of activities varying considerably from country to country. In Britain, for example, the Nature Conservancy Council undertakes to acquire and manage nature reserves, to carry out conservation education and research and it also has a statutory advisory function. The limits of its impact can, however, be seen from the fact that although the original government sponsored body was set up in 1949, the total number of national nature reserves acquired in the following thirty years has only been 164, covering a total area of less than 130,000 hectares, less than 1 per cent of the total land area of Great Britain. Moreover, only a little over one quarter of this area is state-owned, the rest being managed under agreements with owners and occupiers. The position in other countries is even less encouraging. There are, for example, only five national nature reserves in the French part of the region. Like many reserves these are not necessarily the best sites, but those that could be acquired. Most, particularly in the lowland areas, are relatively small and are often subject to

Several species suffer both from the loss of their habitat and from being picked or dug up to be planted in gardens. Notable amongst these is the very striking lady's-slipper (*Cypripedium calceolus*) which is now rare throughout north-west Europe. Flowering period: May-June.

disturbance from outside. Nevertheless they have helped to maintain habitats, particularly wetlands, which would otherwise have been reclaimed for agriculture. Perhaps the most successful reserves in the lowlands are those along the coast which have mainly been set up for their bird populations. For example in the Netherlands two of the most important are the island of Texel, an area of 5,500 hectares with more than 250 species of nesting birds, which includes dunes, woodlands, marshes, heathlands and lakes; and Boschplatt, the eastern part of the island of Terschelling, a reserve of 4,400 hectares, mainly of salt marsh and sand-dunes. In Great Britain one of the most important coastal reserves, recently secured, is a 2,200 hectare site on the Ribble estuary, a large area of salt marsh and coastal flats of international importance for water birds.

As well as nature reserves, most of the countries of north-west Europe have set up a number of national parks. In the United States national parks have been created which cover large tracts of unpopulated wilderness and have conservation of the landscape and its wildlife as their primary aims. In north-west Europe these only exist in Fennoscandia, Iceland and to a lesser extent Scotland. The largest is in north Sweden where the Padjelanta park in Lapland covers 204,000 hectares; adjoining this park are three others, giving a combined area of 8,400 square kilometres. Others in Finland and Norway, although smaller, cover large areas of tundra and montane vegetation. In the populated lowlands of the region national parks of this type are not possible. Nevertheless there are a range of national and regional parks in north-west Europe, all of which have the conservation of wildlife as one of their aims and in some cases, for example, the Lüneberger Heide in north-west Germany, include large areas of semi-natural vegetation. The majority of parks are in relatively accessible areas with a considerable resident population. They are usually administered locally, and attempt to reconcile the often conflicting demands of conservation, local agriculture and general access. Although such policies are less than ideal there is no doubt that they have been successful in modifying the developments which would otherwise have taken place and in retaining much of the area's wildlife interest.

Another form of government action, which is relatively inexpensive, is in promoting pro-conservation legislation. In its most direct form, laws have been passed by all the countries of north-west Europe prohibiting the collection (or killing) of endangered species. All these laws contain a national list of protected species; several countries have supplemented this by regional lists, for example for national parks. The need for such legislation is shown by a recent survey sponsored by the Council of Europe which suggests that just over two thousand flowering plants, about one sixth of the European total have become extinct or are considered threatened or vulnerable. In West Germany and the Netherlands comparable figures are 40 per cent and 50 per cent, reflecting the rapid disappearance in these countries of wetland habitats, old grasslands and agricultural weeds. Other legislation, particularly relating to planning law, may also contain clauses relating to wildlife conservation, often through consultation with the national conservation body. A third form of governmental legislation is through international agreements, one of the most recent being the 'Bern Convention' on the 'Conservation of European Wildlife and Natural Habitats' signed in 1979 by eighteen member states of the Council of Europe, the European Economic Community and Finland. Although such conventions may not result in any immediate direct action, they do constrain government policies to some extent so that conservation is taken into account in making decisions.

In a few countries the state does have limited funds to assist private conservation schemes. From what has already been said it will be evident that, for farmers and foresters to modify their activities in order to further conservation, a financial sacrifice is required. Some people contend that farming and forestry should require planning approval just as would an industrial development and that if permission was refused or onerous conditions applied then there would similarly be no question of compensation. Others argue that, since farming and forestry are traditional rural occupations, they should be treated more sympathetically and largely exempt from planning control. In this case, if for conservation reasons limitations are accepted, then compensation should be payable. To be really effective this would amount to a very considerable state subsidy.

The extent to which governments respond to the claims of conservation reflects the degree of concern among the population and in some countries there are well organized private nature conservation bodies. These are especially important in countries such as Britain, Sweden and the Netherlands where there is a long tradition of interest in natural history. In Great Britain, for example, the Society for the Promotion of Nature Conservation, the Royal Society for the Protection of Birds, and the local trusts for nature conservation, which now cover the whole of the country, have succeeded, either on their own or with funds from bodies such as the World Wildlife Fund, in acquiring a range of nature reserves, which in England exceed the area of national nature reserves. Although some are relatively small and only of local interest, private bodies now hold a considerable number of reserves of national value in Britain. A major problem limiting the private acquisition of large sites is the recurrent cost of management, even where voluntary labour is available. Other ways in which private bodies further conservation are by advising local government bodies and by persuading farmers, foresters and developers to take conservation requirements into account. In a number of cases in Britain private bodies have presented the conservation case at public enquiries into proposed developments which have then been refused on these grounds.

The only way in which wildlife can permanently be conserved is by protecting the habitats which individual threatened species rely upon and this is becoming increasingly expensive. The recent British example of the purchase of 2,200 hectares of the Ribble estuary for £1,725,000 is a case in point. In lowland Europe the pressures of urban and agricultural development are such that it would be misleading to pretend that conservation by the state or private bodies is likely to have more than a marginal effect on the overall rate at which our natural and semi-natural habitats, with their plants and animals, are being destroyed. In the uplands and in the mountains and northern parts of the region the outlook is perhaps more optimistic, since although the pressures have increased, the range of habitats are, in general, intact and there are indications that the populations of the species they support are holding their own. Nevertheless the following comment in the 1979 Annual Report of the British Nature Conservancy Council is relevant for all European countries: 'Unless the nation is willing by one means or another to safeguard these crucially important parts of its heritage, we foresee the loss of irreplaceable sites and a harsh judgement by posterity on this generation.'

How to identify wild flowers

Almost everyone sooner or later finds a wild flower that they do not recognize or to which they cannot put a name. If you have a suitable field guide or Flora with you, you can try to identify the plant in the field. If this fails then ideally you should collect the whole plant, including the roots. If it is too large to collect whole, then collect representative parts, note how they fit together and take measurements of the whole plant, particularly of the flowers and leaves. Be sure, when collecting plants, that you are not breaking the law. In Britain, for instance, the Conservation of Wild Creatures and Wild Plants Act makes it an offence for anyone other than an authorized person without reasonable excuse to *uproot any wild plant,* and it is also an offence for *any person* to pick, uproot or destroy any of the twenty-one protected species. In cases of doubt just make notes.

The flower Is the flower single or are there many packed together, the whole resembling a single flower (like a daisy)?

Treat each floral part separately: how many and what colour and shape are the sepals (calyx) and petals (corolla)? Can you distinguish between sepals and petals, do they all look the same, or are either apparently missing? How many stamens are there? Are they all the same, or do they differ in length or shape? What colour are the anthers? Is the filament a simple round stalk, or does it appear more complex? It is particularly important with the calyx, corolla and stamens to note whether they are 'free', such that you can remove each individually without affecting any of the others (as in a buttercup), or whether they are 'fused'. Fused parts mean that adjacent members are firmly fixed together, for instance petals in the foxglove are fused to form a tube. Often stamens can be fused to petals, or to themselves. The final part of the flower is the ovary. This can have a variety of forms. Is there only one ovary, like the poppy, or are they many small ovaries, as in the buttercup? If there are only a few ovaries, note their number and shape. If there is only a

single ovary, note whether it is superior, above the insertion of the calyx, corolla and stamens (as in the poppy), or whether it is inferior, below the insertion of the other floral parts (as in an *Iris*). Next note the number of styles (if present) and the form of the stigma on each; is it simple, club-shaped, branched and, if so, how many branches does it have? Most ovaries have a number of compartments (cells) within which the seeds are found, as for example the two or three usually found in the tomato. Note the number of cells, and also the overall shape of the ovary.

The inflorescence How are the flowers arranged? Are they solitary, in a raceme, a cyme, an umbel or a capitulum? How long are the flower stalks (pedicels) when the flower is open and when the fruit is mature? Are there any bracts (scale leaves) within the inflorescence? If so, what is their shape, their size, their colour, and how are they arranged?

The fruit For certain groups of plants,

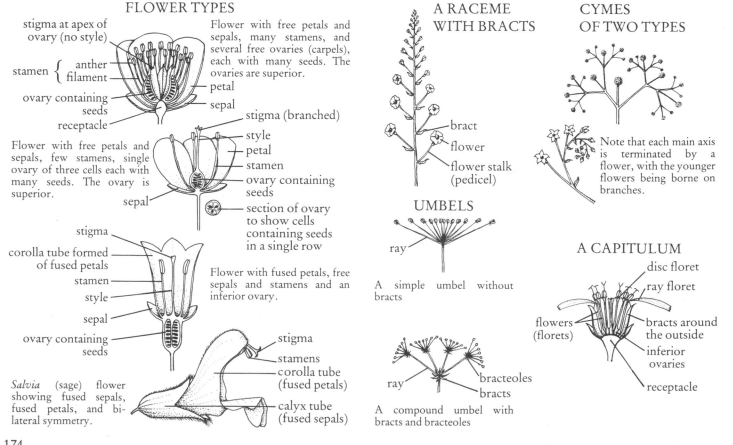

FLOWER TYPES

stigma at apex of ovary (no style)

stamen { anther filament

ovary containing seeds

receptacle

Flower with free petals and sepals, many stamens, and several free ovaries (carpels), each with many seeds. The ovaries are superior.

petal
sepal

Flower with free petals and sepals, few stamens, single ovary of three cells each with many seeds. The ovary is superior.

stigma (branched)
style
petal
stamen
ovary containing seeds
section of ovary to show cells containing seeds in a single row

sepal

stigma

corolla tube formed of fused petals

stamen

style

sepal

ovary containing seeds

Flower with fused petals, free sepals and stamens and an inferior ovary.

Salvia (sage) flower showing fused sepals, fused petals, and bi-lateral symmetry.

stigma
stamens
corolla tube (fused petals)
calyx tube (fused sepals)

A RACEME WITH BRACTS

bract
flower
flower stalk (pedicel)

UMBELS

ray

A simple umbel without bracts

ray
bracteoles
bracts

A compound umbel with bracts and bracteoles

CYMES OF TWO TYPES

Note that each main axis is terminated by a flower, with the younger flowers being borne on branches.

A CAPITULUM

disc floret
ray floret

flowers (florets)
bracts around the outside
inferior ovaries
receptacle

particularly the crucifers (cabbage family), it is particularly important to collect mature fruit. Is the fruit fleshy? If so, does it contain many seeds (a berry) or a single seed (a drupe)? If it is dry, note carefully its shape, size, and how it opens (if it does). What colour is the fruit, how are the seeds arranged in each cell, in a single row, a double row, attached to the centre or to the outside? Is there anything unusual about the fruit, e.g. hairs, spines, hooks?

The leaves Note the shape of the leaves, paying particular attention to how the leaf blade (lamina) joins the leaf stalk (petiole). Does the shape and size of the leaf vary with its position on the plant? Is there a petiole, or is the lamina joined directly to the stem, in which case does the base of the lamina clasp the stem? Are there stipules (small leaf-like structures at the junction of stem and petiole) and if so, how large and what shape are they? Is the leaf hairy? If so, what type of hair: long, short, bristly, woolly, silky? Are the hairs arranged in any particular way or just at random; on both sides of the leaf or just one? Are the hairs simple or branched? Are the leaves distributed evenly up the stem, or are they confined to certain regions? What colour are the leaves? Are they arranged in pairs, in whorls of more than two (how many?), singly in a spiral, singly in ranks, or in another way?

The stem Is it woody? What shape is its cross-section, e.g. square, round? What is its colour and its hairiness? Is it branched? What is its general form? Are there any stolons (like strawberry runners)? If so, what do they look like? If it is a tree, note the type of bark and the type and colour of buds on the twigs.

The underground parts Is there an underground organ such as a bulb, corm or rhizome? If so, what form does the organ take? Are the shoots arising from it densely packed, or do they arise singly and some distance from each other? What sort of roots are present? Are they thick, fleshy and rarely branched, woody, or thin and much branched?

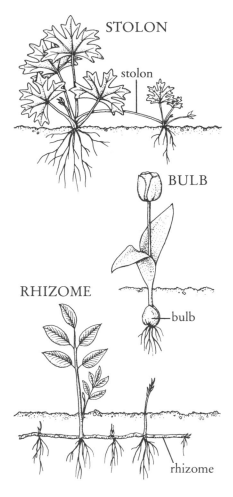

General form of the plant Is it a tree, shrub or herb? Does it climb or scramble over other vegetation? Is it an annual, biennial or perennial? Does it remind you of something you do know? Are there any other interesting features?

Its habitat What sort of vegetation does it grow in? Note the surroundings, rock type, wetness of soil, type of soil, locality, etc. Note any plants you do know that are growing with it.

If you have managed to make notes on all the features mentioned above, then you should be able to identify the plant. Of course, as you gain experience, you will know which are the important features for the particular plant you are studying, and so can leave out much of the above description. A good colour photograph of the plant can be of great help. To help to identify plants, you will need some sort of Flora, a book which gives full identification details. For beginners, a good start is *Wild flowers of Britain and Northern Europe* by R. Fitter, A. Fitter and M. Blamey, published by Collins. Unfortunately it will not enable you to identify every plant in north-west Europe. If the plant you have found is not in that book, then you will have to consult a specialist book. There is only one book that covers the complete flora of Europe, and that is the five volume work, in English, *Flora Europaea*, edited by T. G. Tutin and others, and published by Cambridge University Press. The countries in our region have their own Floras, enabling identification of all their plants. The following, though written in the language of the country they refer to, can be used without too much difficulty.

The Flora of the British Isles (or its smaller companion, *The Excursion Flora of the British Isles*), by A. R. Clapham, T. G. Tutin and E. F. Warburg, published by Cambridge University Press, 1962(80).

An Irish Flora, by D. A. Webb, published by Dundalgan Press Ltd, Dundalk, 1977.

Nouvelle Flore de la Belgique, du Grand-Duché de Luxembourg, du Nord de la France et les Regions voisines (New Flora of Belgium, Luxembourg, Northern France and neighbouring regions), by J. E. de Langhe and others, published by the Patrimoine du Jardin Botanique national de Belgique, Brussels, 1973.

Les quatres Flores de la France, Corse comprise (Flora of France including Corsica), by P. Fournier, published by P. Lechevalier, Paris, 1961.

Flora van Nederland (Dutch Flora), by H. Heukels & S. J. Ooststroom, published by Wolters-Noordhoff, Groningen, 1977.

Den danske Flora (Danish Flora), by C. A. Jorgensen, published by Gyldendal, Copenhagen, 1973.

Flora von Deutschland (Flora of Germany), by O. Schmeil & J. Fitshen, published by Quelle & Meyer, Heidelburg, 1970, *or* Gustav Fischer, Jena, 1958.

Norsk og Svensk Flora (Flora of Norway and Sweden), Johannes Lid, published by Det Norske Samlaget, Oslo, 1974.

Suomen Kasvio (Finnish Flora) by H. I. A. Hiitonen, published by Kustannusosakeyhtiö Otava, Helsinki, 1933.

Islensk Ferdaflora (Icelandic Excursion Flora), by Áskell Löve, published in Reykjavik, 1970.

Glossary

Aapamire A large, slightly sloping mire system with numerous interlocking peat ridges (strings) at right angles to the slope, between which are flat, very wet depressions (flarks).

Anaerobic Lacking oxygen

Base-poor Soil or water that has a lower than average content of substances such as potassium, magnesium, calcium, sodium or iron.

Base-rich Soil or water that has a higher than average content of substances such as potassium, calcium, magnesium, sodium or iron.

Blow-out An area where the wind has removed large quantities of sand from a fixed or semi-fixed dune.

Brashing Removal of dead and poorly growing lower branches from trees in a plantation.

Calcicole A plant that is apparently restricted to soils containing high levels of calcium.

Calcifuge A plant that is apparently restricted to soils containing low levels of calcium.

Climax The apparently stable vegetation that is best suited to a particular site.

Compaction The process by which spaces between soil particles are compressed, making drainage, aeration and root penetration more difficult.

Coppice A system of woodland exploitation whereby trees and shrubs are cut to the base, leaving **stools**, from which several straight stems grow.

Dicotyledons One of the two major groups of flowering plants. It comprises all those having two cotyledons (seed-leaves). Plants such as grasses, sedges, rushes, lilies, irises and aroids have only one seed-leaf and are **monocotyledons.**

Dune-slack An area between dune ridges where the sand is firm and usually moist, being close to the water-table.

Esker A narrow sinuous ridge of river gravels or sands deposited on the bed of a river flowing within a large glacier or ice-sheet, and exposed when the ice melts.

Eutrophic Water rich in nutrients.

Exotic species Those plants introduced into an area where they do not naturally occur.

Fell-field Flattish areas on mountains composed of a jumble of rocks of various sizes with very little vegetation.

Firn-line The altitude at which more snow falls in a year than melts.

Flush An area of ground that has been enriched in mineral nutrients, either dissolved in water or as dry particles, so that the vegetation is more luxuriant.

Frost-heaving Movement of soils and rocks caused by the expansion of water as it freezes beneath them.

Garrigue Dry, shrubby heaths typical of the mediterranean region.

Glacial outwash deposits Areas, usually of sand, gravel and pebbles, deposited by rivers or streams carrying water and materials derived from melting glaciers.

Halophyte A plant that is tolerant of high salt concentrations.

High forest Woodlands where the trees have been allowed to grow fairly densely to maturity, giving relatively tall, straight trees with few shrubs.

Hydrosere The series of vegetational and environmental changes that lead from open water to relatively dry land or mire.

Indicator species A species characteristic of a particular zone or habitat.

Lapse-rate The rate at which temperatures decrease with an increase of altitude.

Leaching Removal of minerals from the soil by water.

Ley A grassland sown on to prepared farmland and cultivated as a crop for a relatively short period before being ploughed up again.

Loess Deposits of very fine-grained silt brought by the wind from the dry surfaces of glacial deposits exposed by the melting of the large ice-sheets at the end of the last glaciation.

Mica-schist Schists containing large amounts of the mineral mica.

Minerotrophic Mires that develop under the influence of water that has been in contact with the surrounding rock or soil.

Monocotyledon See **Dicotyledon.**

Mor Acid, poorly-decomposed humus.

Moraine Debris, often in the form of mounds or ridges, deposited by a glacier or ice sheet.

Mull A neutral, well-decomposed humus.

Oligotrophic Refers to waters having very low nutrient contents.

Ombrotrophic Mires irrigated directly and exclusively by rain, and deriving their nutrient supply entirely from this source.

Outwash fan An area of **glacial outwash deposit** resembling a fan in shape.

Palsamire A mire type characterized by a series of large mounds, up to 10m high and containing a permanently frozen core of peat and silt, set in a fairly level wet poor fen or bog.

Pan A depression in the saltmarsh that has little or no vegetation, relatively steep sides and no drainage exits.

Podzol A soil type characterized by a layer of acid humus (**mor**) on top, a layer of bleached sandy soil from which minerals have been removed, and a layer where these minerals are redeposited.

Poor fen A **minerotrophic** mire that is low in mineral and nutrient contents and often fairly acid.

Prothallus In ferns this is a small, free-living, sexual stage in the life cycle. It is usually a flat plate of tissue.

Rain-shadow an area to the leeward side of a mountain chain that receives a lower than expected rainfall.

Relict species A species now restricted to a very small area, but formerly much more widespread.

Rich fen A **minerotrophic** mire that is rich in dissolved nutrients, often calcium.

Schwingmoor A mire developing from a layer of vegetation and peat floating on the surface of a small, deep, steep-sided pool.

Scree An unstable accumulation of rock fragments on mountainsides.

Snow-lie The length of time that snow covers the ground.

Solifluction The slow movement of soil down a slope caused by the alternate expansion and contraction of water within the soil as it freezes and thaws.

Stoma The minute holes in the leaf through which carbon dioxide passes into the spaces within the leaf and water vapour passes out.

Stools Stumps left after a tree is cut down for **coppice,** from which straight stems grow.

Stratified soil A soil that shows distinct signs of layering.

Structured soil Soil in which the particles are aggregated into crumbs.

Sub-fossil Plant material that is found more or less unchanged deep in sediments.

Substrate The underlying layers of soil or rock.

Succession The process of vegetational change that eventually leads to a **climax.**

Ultrabasic rocks Rocks with a high content of magnesium, iron and other metals, but with very low contents of sodium, potassium and calcium.

Viviparous Having flowers replaced by small, detachable plantlets.

Water-table The level in soil, rock or peat at which standing water is encountered.

Index

If only one page number appears after the scientific name of a plant, the full index entry can be found under the common name. To find the common name, look up the page referred to, where the common and scientific names appear together.

Page numbers in *italics* refer to illustrations.

Acknowledgements
Artists
Paul Brooks (John Martin & Artists), David Etchell/John Ridyard, The Garden Studio (Jane Fern, Josephine Martin, Bridget McGlaughlin), Will Giles, Lesley MacKinnon, Amanda Severne, Shirley Tuckley, Michael Woods.
Maps by Geographical Products

Photographers
A-Z Botanical Collection, Heather Angel, Aquila Photographics, G. G. Aymonin, Alan Baker, Anders Bohlin, Henri Chaumeton, John Clegg, Ecology Pictures, Trevor Elkington, Ron & Christine Foord, Robert Gibbons, C. H. Gimingham, Geoffrey Halliday, E. A. Janes, Friedrich Jantzen, Reijo Juurinen, Seppo Keranen, Knudsens Fotosenter, Mauri Kuokkanen, R. I. Lewis Smith, Pat Livermore, Luonnonkuva-Arkisto, Jorma Luhta, Andrew Malloch, The Natural History Photographic Agency, Teijo Nikkanen, E. Nilsson, Markku Nironen, Lennart Norstrom, Desmond and Marjorie Parish, C. Nilsson, Frank Perring, Donald Pigott, John Proctor, Arno Rautavaara, Leena Saraste, Hugh Simpson, Hugo Sjörs, Kari Soveri, Odd Vevle, H Viitasola, Brian Wheeler.

Index by Celia Davis